Chapter 13 Resource Masters

Algebra 2

$f(x) = -0.5x^2$

O

x

CONSUMABLE WORKBOOKS Many of the worksheets contained in the Chapter Resource Masters booklets are available as consumable workbooks in both English and Spanish.

	ISBN10	ISBN13
Study Guide and Intervention Workbook	0-07-890861-2	978-0-07-890861-3
Homework Practice Workbook	0-07-890862-0	978-0-07-890862-0

Spanish Version

Homework Practice Workbook	0-07-890866-3	978-0-07-890866-8

Answers For Workbooks The answers for Chapter 13 of these workbooks can be found in the back of this Chapter Resource Masters booklet.

StudentWorks Plus™ This CD-ROM includes the entire Student Edition text along with the English workbooks listed above.

TeacherWorks Plus™ All of the materials found in this booklet are included for viewing, printing, and editing in this CD-ROM.

Spanish Assessment Masters (ISBN10: 0-07-890869-8, ISBN13: 978-0-07-890869-9) These masters contain a Spanish version of Chapter 13 Test Form 2A and Form 2C.

The McGraw·Hill Companies

 Glencoe

Send all inquiries to:
Glencoe/McGraw-Hill
8787 Orion Place
Columbus, OH 43240

ISBN: 978-0-07-890538-4
MHID: 0-07-890538-9

Printed in the United States of America.

2 3 4 5 6 7 8 9 10 045 14 13 12 11 10 09

Contents

Teacher's Guide to Using the Chapter 13
  Resource Masters iv

Chapter Resources
Student-Built Glossary 1
Anticipation Guide (English) 3
Anticipation Guide (Spanish) 4

Lesson 13-1
Trigonometric Functions in Right Triangles
Study Guide and Intervention 5
Skills Practice 7
Practice 8
Word Problem Practice 9
Enrichment 10

Lesson 13-2
Angles and Angle Measure
Study Guide and Intervention 11
Skills Practice 13
Practice 14
Word Problem Practice 15
Enrichment 16

Lesson 13-3
Trigonometric Functions of General Angles
Study Guide and Intervention 17
Skills Practice 19
Practice 20
Word Problem Practice 21
Enrichment 22

Lesson 13-4
Law of Sines
Study Guide and Intervention 23
Skills Practice 25
Practice 26
Word Problem Practice 27
Enrichment 28

Lesson 13-5
Law of Cosines
Study Guide and Intervention 29
Skills Practice 30
Practice 32
Word Problem Practice 33
Enrichment 34

Lesson 13-6
Circular Functions
Study Guide and Intervention 35
Skills Practice 37
Practice 38
Word Problem Practice 39
Enrichment 40

Lesson 13-7
Graphing Trigonometric Functions
Study Guide and Intervention 41
Skills Practice 43
Practice 44
Word Problem Practice 45
Enrichment 46

Lesson 13-8
Translations of Trigonometric Graphs
Study Guide and Intervention 47
Skills Practice 49
Practice 50
Word Problem Practice 51
Enrichment 52

Lesson 13-9
Inverse Trigonometric Functions
Study Guide and Intervention 53
Skills Practice 55
Practice 56
Word Problem Practice 57
Enrichment 58

Assessment
Student Recording Sheet 59
Rubric for Scoring Extended Response 60
Chapter 13 Quizzes 1 and 2 61
Chapter 13 Quizzes 3 and 4 62
Chapter 13 Mid-Chapter Test 63
Chapter 13 Vocabulary Test 64
Chapter 13 Test, Form 1 65
Chapter 13 Test, Form 2A 67
Chapter 13 Test, Form 2B 69
Chapter 13 Test, Form 2C 71
Chapter 13 Test, Form 2D 73
Chapter 13 Test, Form 3 75
Chapter 13 Extended Response Test 77
Standardized Test Practice 78

Answers A1–A38

Teacher's Guide to Using the
Chapter 13 Resource Masters

The *Chapter 13 Resource Masters* includes the core materials needed for Chapter 13. These materials include worksheets, extensions, and assessment options. The answers for these pages appear at the back of this booklet.

All of the materials found in this booklet are included for viewing and printing on the *TeacherWorks Plus*™ CD-ROM.

Chapter Resources

Student-Built Glossary (pages 1–2) These masters are a student study tool that presents up to twenty of the key vocabulary terms from the chapter. Students are to record definitions and/or examples for each term. You may suggest that students highlight or star the terms with which they are not familiar. Give this to students before beginning *Lesson 13-1*. Encourage them to add these pages to their mathematics study notebooks. Remind them to complete the appropriate words as they study each lesson.

Anticipation Guide (pages 3–4) This master, presented in both English and Spanish, is a survey used before beginning the chapter to pinpoint what students may or may not know about the concepts in the chapter. Students will revisit this survey after they complete the chapter to see if their perceptions have changed.

Lesson Resources

Study Guide and Intervention These masters provide vocabulary, key concepts, additional worked-out examples and *Check Your Progress* exercises to use as a reteaching activity. It can also be used in conjunction with the *Student Edition* as an instructional tool for students who have been absent.

Skills Practice This master focuses more on the computational nature of the lesson. Use as an additional practice option or as homework for second-day teaching of the lesson.

Practice This master closely follows the types of problems found in the *Exercises* section of the *Student Edition* and includes word problems. Use as an additional practice option or as homework for second-day teaching of the lesson.

Word Problem Practice This master includes additional practice in solving word problems that apply the concepts of the lesson. Use as an additional practice or as homework for second-day teaching of the lesson.

Enrichment These activities may extend the concepts of the lesson, offer an historical or multicultural look at the concepts, or widen students' perspectives on the mathematics they are learning. They are written for use with all levels of students.

Graphing Calculator, TI–Nspire, or Spreadsheet Activities These activities present ways in which technology can be used with the concepts in some lessons of this chapter. Use as an alternative approach to some concepts or as an integral part of your lesson presentation.

Assessment Options

The assessment masters in the *Chapter 13 Resource Masters* offer a wide range of assessment tools for formative (monitoring) assessment and summative (final) assessment.

Student Recording Sheet This master corresponds with the standardized test practice at the end of the chapter.

Extended Response Rubric This master provides information for teachers and students on how to assess performance on open-ended questions.

Quizzes Four free-response quizzes offer assessment at appropriate intervals in the chapter.

Mid-Chapter Test This 1-page test provides an option to assess the first half of the chapter. It parallels the timing of the *Mid-Chapter* Quiz in the *Student Edition* and includes both multiple-choice and free-response questions.

Vocabulary Test This test is suitable for all students. It includes a list of vocabulary words and 10 questions to assess students' knowledge of those words. This can also be used in conjunction with one of the leveled chapter tests.

Leveled Chapter Tests

- *Form 1* contains multiple-choice questions and is intended for use with below grade level students.

- *Forms 2A and 2B* contain multiple-choice questions aimed at on grade level students. These tests are similar in format to offer comparable testing situations.

- *Forms 2C and 2D* contain free-response questions aimed at on grade level students. These tests are similar in format to offer comparable testing situations.

- *Form 3* is a free-response test for use with above grade level students.

All of the above mentioned tests include a free-response Bonus question.

Extended-Response Test Performance assessment tasks are suitable for all students. Sample answers and a scoring rubric are included for evaluation.

Standardized Test Practice These three pages are cumulative in nature. It includes three parts: multiple-choice questions with bubble-in answer format, griddable questions with answer grids, and short-answer free-response questions.

Answers

- The answers for the *Anticipation Guide* and *Lesson Resources* are provided as reduced pages.

- Full-size answer keys are provided for the assessment masters.

13 | Student-Built Glossary

This is an alphabetical list of the key vocabulary terms you will learn in Chapter 13. As you study the chapter, complete each term's definition or description. Remember to add the page number where you found the term. Add these pages to your Algebra Study Notebook to review vocabulary at the end of the chapter.

Vocabulary Term	Found on Page	Definition/Description/Example
angle of depression		
angle of elevation		
amplitude		
circular function		
cosecant (KOH·SEE·KANT)		
cosine		
cotangent		
cycle		
frequency		
Law of Cosines		

(continued on the next page)

13 Student-Built Glossary

Vocabulary Term	Found on Page	Definition/Description/Example
Law of Sines		
period		
periodic function		
radian (RAY·dee·uhn)		
secant		
sine		
standard position		
tangent		
trigonometry (THRIH·guh·NAH·muh·tree)		
unit circle		

13 Anticipation Guide

Trigonometric Functions

Step 1   *Before you begin Chapter 13*

- Read each statement.

- Decide whether you Agree (A) or Disagree (D) with the statement.

- Write A or D in the first column OR if you are not sure whether you agree or disagree, write NS (Not Sure).

STEP 1 A, D, or NS	Statement	STEP 2 A or D
	1. The tangent of an acute angle in a right triangle is the ratio of the side adjacent to the angle and the side opposite the angle.	
	2. Solving a triangle means finding the measures of all side lengths and all angles.	
	3. A radian is the measure of an angle in standard position whose rays intercept an arc length of 1 unit on the unit circle.	
	4. A reference angle always measures between 90° and 180°.	
	5. In cases where the Law of Sines can be used to solve a triangle, the Law of Sines always produces a unique solution.	
	6. The Law of Sines can be used to solve a triangle when two angles and any side of the triangle are given.	
	7. The Law of Cosines can be used to solve a triangle when all three sides of the triangle are given.	
	8. The sine and cosine functions each have a period of 180°.	
	9. The relation represented by $y = \sin^{-1} x$ is not a function, but the relation represented by $y = \text{Sin}^{-1} x$ is a function.	
	10. An angle is in standard position if it has its vertex at the origin and its initial side is along the positive y-axis.	

Step 2   *After you complete Chapter 13*

- Reread each statement and complete the last column by entering an A or a D.

- Did any of your opinions about the statements change from the first column?

- For those statements that you mark with a D, use a piece of paper to write an example of why you disagree.

13 Ejercicios preparatorios

Funciones trigonométricas

- Lee cada enunciado.

- Decide si estás de acuerdo (A) o en desacuerdo (D) con el enunciado.

- Escribe A o D en la primera columna O si no estás seguro(a) de la respuesta, escribe NS (No estoy seguro(a)).

PASO 1 A, D o NS	Enunciado	PASO 2 A o D
	1. La tangente de un ángulo agudo en un triángulo rectángulo es la razón del lado adyacente al ángulo y el lado opuesto al ángulo.	
	2. Resolver un triángulo significa hallar las medidas de las longitudes de todos los lados y de todos los ángulos.	
	3. Un radián es una medida de un ángulo en posición estándar cuyos rayos intersecan un arco de 1 unidad en la unidad del círculo.	
	4. Un ángulo de referencia siempre mide entre 90° y 180°.	
	5. En casos donde se puede usar la ley de los senos para resolver un triángulo, dicha ley siempre produce una solución única.	
	6. La ley de los senos se puede usar para resolver un triángulo cuando se conocen dos ángulos y cualquier lado del triángulo.	
	7. La ley de los senos se puede usar para resolver un triángulo cuando se conocen todos los tres lados del triángulo.	
	8. Tanto la función seno como la coseno tienen un período de 180°.	
	9. La relación representada por $y = \sin^{-1} x$ no es una función, pero la relación representada por $y = \text{Sin}^{-1} x$ es una función	
	10. Un ángulo está en posición estándar si tiene su vértice en el origen y su lado inicial yace a lo largo de eje y positivo.	

- Lee cada enunciado y completa la última columna contestando A o D.

- ¿Cambió cualquiera de tus opiniones sobre los enunciados de la primera columna?

- En una hoja de papel aparte, escribe un ejemplo de por qué estás en desacuerdo con los enunciados que marcaste con una D.

13-1 Study Guide and Intervention

Trigonometric Functions in Right Triangles

Trigonometric Functions for Acute Angles Trigonometry is the study of relationships among the angles and sides of a right triangle. A **trigonometric function** has a rule given by a **trigonometric ratio**, which is a ratio that compares the side lengths of a right triangle.

Trigonometric Functions in Right Triangles	If θ is the measure of an acute angle of a right triangle, *opp* is the measure of the leg opposite θ, *adj* is the measure of the leg adjacent to θ, and *hyp* is the measure of the hypotenuse, then the following are true.
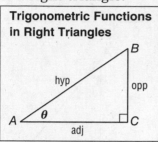	$\sin \theta = \dfrac{opp}{hyp} \qquad \cos \theta = \dfrac{adj}{hyp} \qquad \tan \theta = \dfrac{opp}{adj}$ $\csc \theta = \dfrac{hyp}{opp} \qquad \sec \theta = \dfrac{hyp}{adj} \qquad \cot \theta = \dfrac{adj}{opp}$

Example   In a right triangle, $\angle B$ is acute and $\cos B = \dfrac{3}{7}$. Find the value of $\tan B$.

Step 1   Draw a right triangle and label one acute angle B. Label the adjacent side 3 and the hypotenuse 7.

Step 2   Use the Pythagorean Theorem to find b.

$a^2 + b^2 = c^2$ Pythagorean Theorem

$3^2 + b^2 = 7^2$ $a = 3$ and $c = 7$

$9 + b^2 = 49$ Simplify.

$b^2 = 40$ Subtract 9 from each side.

$b = \sqrt{40} = 2\sqrt{10}$ Take the positive square root of each side.

Step 3   Find $\tan B$.

$\tan B = \dfrac{opp}{adj}$ Tangent function

$\tan B = \dfrac{2\sqrt{10}}{3}$ Replace *opp* with $2\sqrt{10}$ and *adj* with 3.

Exercises

Find the values of the six trigonometric functions for angle θ.

1.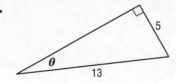

2.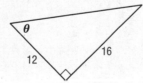

3.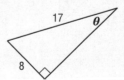

In a right triangle, $\angle A$ and $\angle B$ are acute.

4. If $\tan A = \dfrac{7}{12}$, what is $\cos A$?

5. If $\cos A = \dfrac{1}{2}$, what is $\tan A$?

6. If $\sin B = \dfrac{3}{8}$, what is $\tan B$?

13-1 | **Study Guide and Intervention** *(continued)*

Trigonometric Functions in Right Triangles

Use Trigonometric Functions You can use trigonometric functions to find missing side lengths and missing angle measures of right triangles. You can find the measure of the missing angle by using the inverse of sine, cosine, or tangent.

Example | **Find the measure of ∠C. Round to the nearest tenth if necessary.**

You know the measure of the side opposite ∠C and the measure of the hypotenuse. Use the sine function.

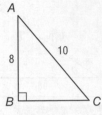

$$\sin C = \frac{\text{opp}}{\text{hyp}}$$ Sine function

$$\sin C = \frac{8}{10}$$ Replace *opp* with 8 and *hyp* with 10.

$$\sin^{-1}\frac{8}{10} = m\angle C$$ Inverse sine

$$53.1° \approx m\angle C$$ Use a calculator.

Exercises

Use a trigonometric function to find each value of x. Round to the nearest tenth if necessary.

1.

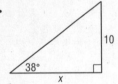

2.

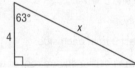

3.

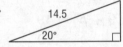

4.

5.

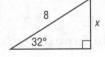

6.

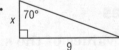

Find x. Round to the nearest tenth if necessary.

7.

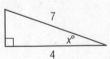

8.

9.

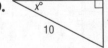

13-1 Skills Practice

Trigonometric Functions in Right Triangles

Find the values of the six trigonometric functions for angle θ.

1.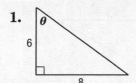

2.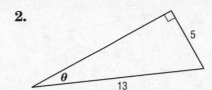

3.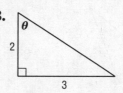

In a right triangle, ∠A is acute.

4. If $\tan A = 3$, what is $\sin A$?

5. If $\sin A = \frac{1}{16}$, what is $\cos A$?

Use a trigonometric function to find the value of x. Round to the nearest tenth if necessary.

6.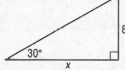

7.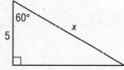

8.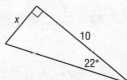

9.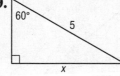

10.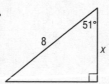

11.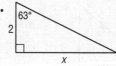

Find the value of x. Round to the nearest tenth if necessary.

12.

13.

14.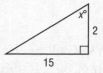

Lesson 13-1

13-1 Practice

Trigonometric Functions in Right Triangles

Find the values of the six trigonometric functions for angle θ.

1.

2.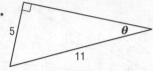

3.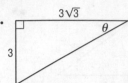

In a right triangle, $\angle A$ and $\angle B$ are acute.

4. If $\tan B = 2$, what is $\cos B$? 5. If $\tan A = \frac{11}{17}$, what is $\sin A$? 6. If $\sin B = \frac{8}{15}$, what is $\cos B$?

Use a trigonometric function to find each value of x. Round to the nearest tenth if necessary.

7.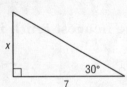

8.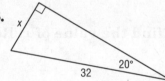

9.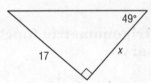

Use trigonometric functions to find the values of x and y. Round to the nearest tenth if necessary.

10.

11.

12.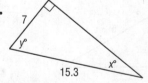

13. **SURVEYING** John stands 150 meters from a water tower and sights the top at an angle of elevation of 36°. If John's eyes are 2 meters above the ground, how tall is the tower? Round to the nearest meter.

13-1 **Word Problem Practice**

Trigonometric Functions in Right Triangles

1. ROOFS The roof on a house is built with a pitch of 10/12, meaning that the roof rises 10 feet for every 12 feet of horizontal run. The side view of the roof is shown in the figure below.

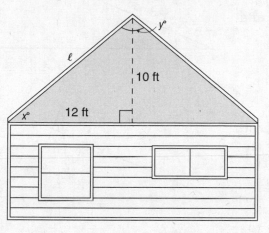

a. What is the angle x at the base of the roof?

b. What is the angle y at the peak of the roof?

c. What is the length ℓ of the roof?

d. If the width of the roof is 26 feet, what is the total area of the roof?

2. BUILDINGS Jessica stands 150 feet from the base of a tall building. She measures the angle from her eye to the top of the building to be 84°. If her eye level is 5 feet above the ground, how tall is the building?

3. SCALE DRAWING The collection pool for a fountain is in the shape of a right triangle. A scale drawing shows that the angles of the triangle are 40°, 50°, and 90°. If the hypotenuse of the actual fountain will be 30 feet, what are the lengths of the other two sides of the fountain?

4. GEOMETRY A regular hexagon is inscribed in a circle with a diameter of 8 inches.

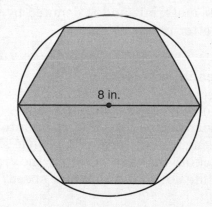

a. What is the perimeter of the hexagon?

b. What is the area of the hexagon?

Lesson 13-1

13-1 Enrichment

The Angle of Repose

Suppose you place a block of wood on an inclined plane, as shown at the right. If the angle, θ, at which the plane is inclined from the horizontal is very small, the block will not move. If you increase the angle, the block will eventually overcome the force of friction and start to slide down the plane.

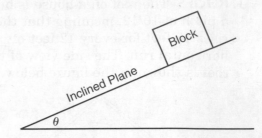

At the instant the block begins to slide, the angle formed by the plane is called the angle of friction, or the angle of repose.

For situations in which the block and plane are smooth but unlubricated, the angle of repose depends *only* on the types of materials in the block and the plane. The angle is independent of the area of contact between the two surfaces and of the weight of the block.

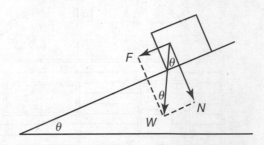

The drawing at the right shows how to use vectors to find a coefficient of friction. This coefficient varies with different materials and is denoted by the Greek letter mu, μ.

$$F = W \sin \theta \qquad N = W \cos \theta$$
$$F = \mu N$$
$$\mu = \frac{\sin \theta}{\cos \theta} = \tan \theta$$

Solve each problem.

Material	Coefficient of Friction μ
Wood on wood	0.5
Wood on stone	0.5
Rubber tire on dry concrete	1.0
Rubber tire on wet concrete	0.7

1. A wooden chute is built so that wooden crates can slide down into the basement of a store. What angle should the chute make in order for the crates to slide down at a constant speed?

2. Will a 100-pound wooden crate slide down a stone ramp that makes an angle of 20° with the horizontal? Explain your answer.

3. If you increase the weight of the crate in Exercise 2 to 300 pounds, does it change your answer?

4. A car with rubber tires is being driven on dry concrete pavement. If the car tires spin without traction on a hill, how steep is the hill?

5. For Exercise 4, does it make a difference if it starts to rain? Explain your answer.

13-2 Study Guide and Intervention

Angles and Angle Measure

Angles in Standard Position An angle is determined by two rays. The degree measure of an angle in standard position is described by the amount and direction of rotation from the **initial side**, which lies along the positive x-axis, to the **terminal side**. A counterclockwise rotation is associated with positive angle measure and a clockwise rotation is associated with negative angle measure. Two or more angles in standard position with the same terminal side are called **coterminal angles**.

Example 1 **Draw an angle with measure 290° in standard position.**

The negative y-axis represents a positive rotation of 270°. To generate an angle of 290°, rotate the terminal side 20° more in the counterclockwise direction

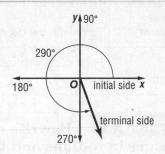

Example 2 **Find an angle with a positive measure and an angle with a negative measure that are coterminal with each angle.**

a. 250°

A positive angle is 250° + 360° or 610°.   Add 360°.

A negative angle is 250° − 360° or −110°.   Subtract 360°.

b. −140°

A positive angle is −140° + 360° or 220°.   Add 360°.

A negative angle is −140° − 360° or −500°.   Subtract 360°.

Exercises

Draw an angle with the given measure in standard position.

1. 160°   **2.** 280°   **3.** 400°

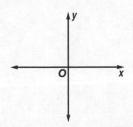   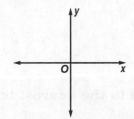   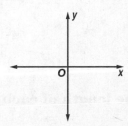

Find an angle with a positive measure and an angle with a negative measure that are coterminal with each angle.

4. 65°   **5.** −75°   **6.** 230°   **7.** 420°

Lesson 13-2

13-2 Study Guide and Intervention *(continued)*

Angles and Angle Measure

Convert Between Degrees and Radians Angles can be measured in **degrees** and **radians**, which are units based on arc length. One radian is the measure of an angle θ in standard position with a terminal side that intercepts an arc with the same length as the radius of the circle. Degree measure and radian measure are related by the equations 2π radians $= 360°$ and π radians $= 180°$.

Radian and Degree Measure	To rewrite the radian measure of an angle in degrees, multiply the number of radians by $\dfrac{180°}{\pi \text{ radians}}$.
	To rewrite the degree measure of an angle in radians, multiply the number of degrees by $\dfrac{\pi \text{ radians}}{180°}$.
Arc Length	For a circle with radius r and central angle θ (in radians), the arc length s equals the product of r and θ. $$s = r\theta$$

Example 1 Rewrite each degree measure in radians and the radian measure in degrees.

a. $45°$
$$45° = 45°\left(\frac{\pi \text{ radians}}{180°}\right) = \frac{\pi}{4} \text{ radians}$$

b. $\dfrac{5\pi}{3}$ **radians**
$$\frac{5\pi}{3} \text{ radians} = \frac{5\pi}{3}\left(\frac{180°}{\pi}\right) = 300°$$

Example 2 A circle has a radius of 5 cm and central angle of 135°, what is the length of the circle's arc?

Find the central angle in radians.
$$135° = 135°\left(\frac{\pi \text{ radians}}{180°}\right) = \frac{3\pi}{4} \text{ radians}$$

Use the radius and central angle to find the arc length.

$s = r\theta$ Write the formula for arc length.

$\quad = 5 \cdot \dfrac{3\pi}{4}$ Replace r with 5 and θ with $\frac{3\pi}{4}$.

$\quad \approx 11.78$ Use a calculator to simplify.

Exercises

Rewrite each degree measure in radians and each radian measure in degrees.

1. $140°$

2. $-260°$

3. $-\dfrac{3\pi}{5}$

4. $-75°$

5. $\dfrac{7\pi}{6}$

6. $380°$

Find the length of each arc. Round to the nearest tenth.

7.

8.

9.

13-2 Skills Practice

Angles and Angle Measure

Draw an angle with the given measure in standard position.

1. 185°

2. 810°

3. 390°

4. 495°

5. −50°

6. −420°

Find an angle with a positive measure and an angle with a negative measure that are coterminal with each angle.

7. 45°

8. 60°

9. 370°

10. −90°

11. $\frac{2\pi}{3}$

12. $\frac{5\pi}{2}$

13. $\frac{\pi}{6}$

14. $-\frac{3\pi}{4}$

Rewrite each degree measure in radians and each radian measure in degrees.

15. 130°

16. 720°

17. 210°

18. 90°

19. −30°

20. −270°

21. $\frac{\pi}{3}$

22. $\frac{5\pi}{6}$

23. $\frac{2\pi}{3}$

24. $\frac{5\pi}{4}$

25. $-\frac{3\pi}{4}$

26. $-\frac{7\pi}{6}$

Lesson 13-2

13-2 Practice

Angles and Angle Measure

Draw an angle with the given measure in standard position.

1. 210°

2. 305°

3. 580°

4. 135°

5. −450°

6. −560°

Find an angle with a positive measure and an angle with a negative measure that are coterminal with each angle.

7. 65°

8. 80°

9. 110°

10. $\frac{2\pi}{5}$

11. $\frac{5\pi}{6}$

12. $-\frac{3\pi}{2}$

Rewrite each degree measure in radians and each radian measure in degrees.

13. 18°

14. 6°

15. −72°

16. −820°

17. 4π

18. $\frac{5\pi}{2}$

19. $-\frac{9\pi}{2}$

20. $-\frac{7\pi}{12}$

Find the length of each arc. Round to the nearest tenth.

21.

3.5 $\frac{\pi}{2}$

22.

$\frac{3\pi}{2}$ 4.25

23.

$\frac{5\pi}{3}$ 5.62

24. TIME Find both the degree and radian measures of the angle through which the hour hand on a clock rotates from 5 A.M. to 10 P.M.

25. ROTATION A truck with 16-inch radius wheels is driven at 77 feet per second (52.5 miles per hour). Find the measure of the angle through which a point on the outside of the wheel travels each second. Round to the nearest degree and nearest radian.

13-2 Word Problem Practice

Angles and Angle Measure

1. AMUSEMENT PARKS The carousel at an amusement park has 20 horses spaced evenly around its circumference. The horses are numbered consecutively from 1 to 20. The carousel completes one rotation about its axis every 40 seconds.

a. What is the central angle, in degrees, formed by horse #1 and horse #8?

b. What is the speed of the carousel in rotations per minute?

c. What is the speed of the carousel in radians per minute?

d. A child rides the carousel for 6 minutes. Through how many radians will the child pass in the course of the carousel ride?

2. TIME Through what angle, in degrees and radians, does the hour hand on a clock rotate between 4 P.M. and 7 P.M.? Assuming the length of the hour hand is 6 inches, find the arc length of the circle made by the hour hand during that time.

3. TIME Through what angle, in degrees and radians, does the minute hand rotate between 4 P.M. and 7 P.M.?

4. PLANETS Earth makes one full rotation on its axis every 24 hours. How long does it take Earth to rotate through 150°? Neptune makes one full rotation on its axis every 16 hours. How long does it take Neptune to rotate through 150°?

Lesson 13-2

13-2 Enrichment

Making and Using a Hypsometer

A **hypsometer** is a device that can be used to measure the height of an object. To construct your own hypsometer, you will need a rectangular piece of heavy cardboard that is at least 7 cm by 10 cm, a straw, transparent tape, a string about 20 cm long, and a small weight that can be attached to the string.

Mark off 1-cm increments along one short side and one long side of the cardboard. Tape the straw to the other short side. Then attach the weight to one end of the string, and attach the other end of the string to one corner of the cardboard, as shown in the figure below. The diagram below shows how your hypsometer should look.

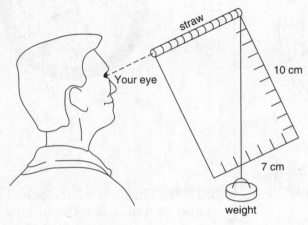

To use the hypsometer, you will need to measure the distance from the base of the object whose height you are finding to where you stand when you use the hypsometer.

Sight the top of the object through the straw. Note where the free-hanging string crosses the bottom scale. Then use similar triangles to find the height of the object.

1. Draw a diagram to illustrate how you can use similar triangles and the hypsometer to find the height of a tall object.

Use your hypsometer to find the height of each of the following.

2. your school's flagpole

3. a tree on your school's property

4. the highest point on the front wall of your school building

5. the goal posts on a football field

6. the hoop on a basketball court

13-3 Study Guide and Intervention

Trigonometric Functions of General Angles

Trigonometric Functions for General Angles

Trigonometric Functions, θ in Standard Position	Let θ be an angle in standard position and let $P(x, y)$ be a point on the terminal side of θ. By the Pythagorean Theorem, the distance r from the origin is given by $r = \sqrt{x^2 + y^2}$. The trigonometric functions of an angle in standard position may be defined as follows.
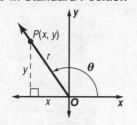	$\sin \theta = \dfrac{y}{r}$ $\qquad$ $\cos \theta = \dfrac{x}{r}$ $\qquad$ $\tan \theta = \dfrac{y}{x}, x \neq 0$ $\csc \theta = \dfrac{r}{y}, y \neq 0$ $\quad$ $\sec \theta = \dfrac{r}{x}, x \neq 0$ $\quad$ $\cot \theta = \dfrac{x}{y}, y \neq 0$

Example Find the exact values of the six trigonometric functions of θ if the terminal side of θ in standard position contains the point $(-5, 5\sqrt{2})$.

You know that $x = -5$ and $y = 5$. You need to find r.

$r = \sqrt{x^2 + y^2}$ $\qquad$ Pythagorean Theorem

$\quad - \sqrt{(-5)^0 + (5\sqrt{2})^2}$ $\qquad$ Replace x with -5 and y with $5\sqrt{2}$.

$\quad = \sqrt{75}$ or $5\sqrt{3}$

Now use $x = -5$, $y = 5\sqrt{2}$, and $r = 5\sqrt{3}$ to write the six trigonometric ratios.

$\sin \theta = \dfrac{y}{r} = \dfrac{5\sqrt{2}}{5\sqrt{3}} = \dfrac{\sqrt{6}}{3}$ $\qquad$ $\cos \theta = \dfrac{x}{r} = \dfrac{-5}{5\sqrt{3}} = -\dfrac{\sqrt{3}}{3}$ $\qquad$ $\tan \theta = \dfrac{y}{x} = \dfrac{5\sqrt{2}}{-5} = -\sqrt{2}$

$\csc \theta = \dfrac{r}{y} = \dfrac{5\sqrt{3}}{5\sqrt{2}} = \dfrac{\sqrt{6}}{2}$ $\qquad$ $\sec \theta = \dfrac{r}{x} = \dfrac{5\sqrt{3}}{-5} = -\sqrt{3}$ $\qquad$ $\cot \theta = \dfrac{x}{y} = \dfrac{-5}{5\sqrt{2}} = -\dfrac{\sqrt{2}}{2}$

Exercises

The terminal side of θ in standard position contains each point. Find the exact values of the six trigonometric functions of θ.

1. $(8, 4)$

2. $(4, 4)$

3. $(0, 4)$

4. $(6, 2)$

Lesson 13-3

13-3 Study Guide and Intervention *(continued)*

Trigonometric Functions of General Angles

Trigonometric Functions with Reference Angles If θ is a nonquadrantal angle in standard position, its **reference angle** θ' is defined as the acute angle formed by the terminal side of θ and the *x*-axis.

Reference Angle Rule				
	Quadrant I $\theta' = \theta$	Quadrant II $\theta' = 180° - \theta$ $(\theta' = \pi - \theta)$	Quadrant III $\theta' = \theta - 180°$ $(\theta' = \theta - \pi)$	Quadrant IV $\theta' = 360° - \theta$ $(\theta' = 2\pi - \theta)$

Example 1 Sketch an angle of measure 205°. Then find its reference angle.

Because the terminal side of 205° lies in Quadrant III, the reference angle θ' is 205° − 180° or 25°.

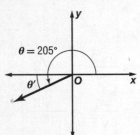

$\theta = 205°$

Example 2 Use a reference angle to find the exact value of $\cos \dfrac{3\pi}{4}$.

Because the terminal side of $\dfrac{3\pi}{4}$ lies in Quadrant II, the reference angle θ' is $\pi - \dfrac{3\pi}{4}$ or $\dfrac{\pi}{4}$.

The cosine function is negative in Quadrant II.

$\cos \dfrac{3\pi}{4} = -\cos \dfrac{\pi}{4} = -\dfrac{\sqrt{2}}{2}$.

Exercises

Sketch each angle. Then find its reference angle.

1. 155°   **2.** 230°   **3.** $\dfrac{4\pi}{3}$ **4.** $-\dfrac{\pi}{6}$

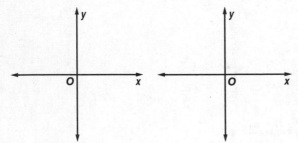
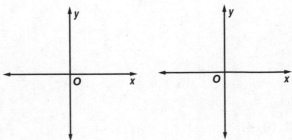

Find the exact value of each trigonometric function.

5. $\tan 330°$ **6.** $\cos \dfrac{11\pi}{4}$ **7.** $\cot 30°$ **8.** $\csc \dfrac{\pi}{4}$

13-3 Skills Practice

Trigonometric Functions of General Angles

The terminal side of θ in standard position contains each point. Find the exact values of the six trigonometric functions of θ.

1. (5, 12)

2. (3, 4)

3. (8, −15)

4. (−4, 3)

5. (−9, −40)

6. (1, 2)

7. (3, −9)

8. (−8, 12)

Sketch each angle. Then find its reference angle.

9. 135°

10. 200°

11. $\dfrac{5\pi}{3}$

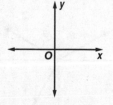
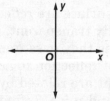
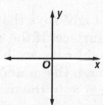

Find the exact value of each trigonometric function.

12. sin 150°

13. cos 270°

14. cot 135°

15. tan (−30°)

16. tan $\dfrac{\pi}{4}$

17. cos $\dfrac{4\pi}{3}$

18. cot (−π)

19. sin $\left(-\dfrac{3\pi}{4}\right)$

Lesson 13-3

13-3 Practice

Trigonometric Functions of General Angles

The terminal side of θ in standard position contains each point. Find the exact values of the six trigonometric functions of θ.

1. $(6, 8)$

2. $(-20, 21)$

3. $(-2, -5)$

Sketch each angle. Then find its reference angle.

4. $\dfrac{13\pi}{8}$

5. $-210°$

6. $-\dfrac{7\pi}{4}$

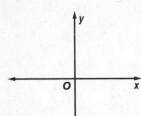

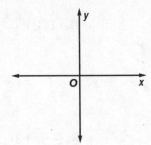

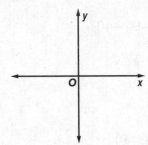

Find the exact value of each trigonometric function.

7. $\tan 135°$

8. $\cot 210°$

9. $\cot(-90°)$

10. $\cos 405°$

11. $\tan \dfrac{5\pi}{3}$

12. $\csc\left(-\dfrac{3\pi}{4}\right)$

13. $\cot 2\pi$

14. $\tan \dfrac{13\pi}{6}$

15. LIGHT Light rays that "bounce off" a surface are *reflected* by the surface. If the surface is partially transparent, some of the light rays are bent or *refracted* as they pass from the air through the material. The angles of reflection θ_1 and of refraction θ_2 in the diagram at the right are related by the equation $\sin \theta_1 = n \sin \theta_2$. If $\theta_1 = 60°$ and $n = \sqrt{3}$, find the measure of θ_2.

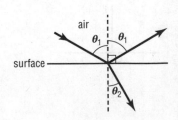

16. FORCE A cable running from the top of a utility pole to the ground exerts a horizontal pull of 800 Newtons and a vertical pull of $800\sqrt{3}$ Newtons. What is the sine of the angle θ between the cable and the ground? What is the measure of this angle?

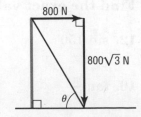

13-3 Word Problem Practice

Trigonometric Functions of General Angles

1. RADIOS Two correspondence radios are located 2 kilometers away from a base camp. The angle formed between the first radio, the base camp, and the second radio is 120°. If the first radio has coordinates (2, 0) relative to the base camp, what is the position of the second radio relative to the base camp?

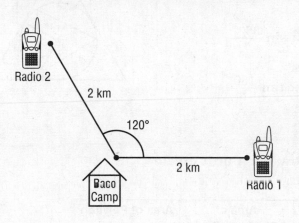

2. CLOCKS The pendulum of a grandfather clock swings back and forth through an arc. The angle θ of the pendulum is given by $\theta = 0.3 \cos\left(\frac{\pi}{2} + 5t\right)$ where t is the time in seconds after leaving the bottom of the swing. Determine the measure of the angles in radians for $t = 0, 0.5, 1, 1.5, 2, 2.5,$ and 3 seconds.

3. FERRIS WHEELS Janice rides a Ferris wheel in Japan called the Sky Dream Fukuoka, which has a radius of about 60 m and is 5 m off the ground. After she enters the bottom car, the wheel rotates 210.5° counterclockwise before stopping. How high above the ground is Janice when the car has stopped?

4. SOCCER Alice kicks a soccer ball towards a wall. The ball is deflected off the wall at an angle of 40°, and it travels 6 meters. How far is the soccer ball from the wall when it stops rolling?

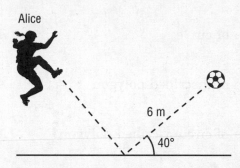

5. PAPER AIRPLANES The formula $R = \dfrac{V_0^2 \sin 2\theta}{32} + 15 \cos \theta$ gives the distance traveled by a paper airplane that is thrown with an initial velocity of V_0 feet per second at an angle of θ with the ground.

a. If the airplane is thrown with an initial velocity of 15 feet per second at an angle of 25°, how far will the airplane travel?

b. Two airplanes are thrown with an initial velocity of 10 feet per second. One airplane is thrown at an angle of 15° to the ground, and the other airplane is thrown at an angle of 45° to the ground. Which will travel farther?

Lesson 13-3

13-3 Enrichment

Areas of Polygons and Circles

A regular polygon has sides of equal length and angles of equal measure.
A regular polygon can be inscribed in or circumscribed about a circle. For
n-sided regular polygons, the following area formulas can be used.

Area of circle $\qquad\qquad\qquad A_C = \pi r^2$

Area of inscribed polygon $\qquad A_I = \dfrac{nr^2}{2} \times \sin\dfrac{360°}{n}$

Area of circumscribed polygon $\qquad A_C = nr^2 \times \tan\dfrac{180°}{n}$

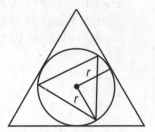

**Use a calculator to complete the chart below for a unit circle
(a circle of radius 1).**

	Number of Sides	Area of Inscribed Polygon	Area of Circle minus Area of Polygon	Area of Circumscribed Polygon	Area of Polygon minus Area of Circle
	3	1.2990381	1.8425545	5.1961524	2.054598
1.	4				
2.	8				
3.	12				
4.	20				
5.	24				
6.	28				
7.	32				
8.	1000				

9. What number do the areas of the circumscribed and inscribed polygons
seem to be approaching?

13-4 Study Guide and Intervention

Law of Sines

Find the Area of a Triangle The area of any triangle is one half the product of the lengths of two sides and the sine of the included angle.

Area of a Triangle	area = $\frac{1}{2}bc \sin A$ area = $\frac{1}{2}ac \sin B$ area = $\frac{1}{2}ab \sin C$	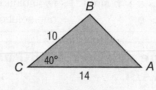

Example Find the area of $\triangle ABC$ to the nearest tenth.

In $\triangle ABC$, $a = 10$, $b = 14$, and $C = 40°$.

Area = $\frac{1}{2}ab \sin C$ Area formula

   = $\frac{1}{2}(10)(14)\sin 40°$ Substitution

   ≈ 44.9951   Simplify.

The area of the triangle is approximately 45 square units.

Exercises

Find the area of $\triangle ABC$ to the nearest tenth, if necessary.

1.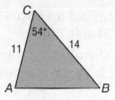

2.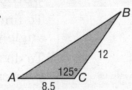

3.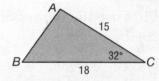

4.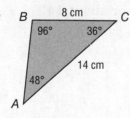

5.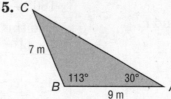

6.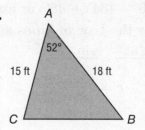

7. $A = 20°$, $c = 4$ cm, $b = 7$ cm

8. $C = 55°$, $a = 10$ m, $b = 15$ m

9. $B = 42°$, $c = 9$ ft, $a = 3$ ft

10. $c = 15$ in., $b = 13$ in., $A = 53°$

11. $a = 12$ cm, $b = 8$ cm, $C = 85°$

Lesson 13-4

13-4 Study Guide and Intervention (continued)

Law of Sines

Use the Law of Sines to Solve Triangles You can use the Law of Sines to solve any triangle if you know the measures of two angles and any side opposite one of the angles, or the measures of two sides and the angle opposite one of them.

Law of Sines	$\dfrac{\sin A}{a} = \dfrac{\sin B}{b} = \dfrac{\sin C}{c}$

	Suppose you are given a, b, and A for a triangle.	
Possible Triangles Given Two Sides and One Opposite Angle	If a is acute: $\quad a < b \sin A \quad \Rightarrow$ no solution $\quad a = b \sin A \quad \Rightarrow$ one solution $\quad b > a > b \sin A \Rightarrow$ two solutions $\quad a > b \qquad\qquad \Rightarrow$ one solution	If A is right or obtuse: $\quad a \leq b \Rightarrow$ no solution $\quad a > b \Rightarrow$ one solution

Example Determine whether $\triangle ABC$ has *no* solutions, *one* solution, or *two* solutions. Then solve $\triangle ABC$.

a. $A = 48°$, $a = 11$, and $b = 16$ Since A is acute, find $b \sin A$ and compare it with a.
$b \sin A = 16 \sin 48° \approx 11.89$ Since $11 < 11.89$, there is no solution.

b. $A = 34°$, $a = 6$, $b = 8$

Since A is acute, find $b \sin A$ and compare it with a; $b \sin A = 8 \sin 34° \approx 4.47$. Since $8 > 6 > 4.47$, there are two solutions. Thus there are two possible triangles to solve.

Acute B

First use the Law of Sines to find B.
$$\frac{\sin B}{8} = \frac{\sin 34°}{6}$$
$$\sin B \approx 0.7456$$
$$B \approx 48°$$

The measure of angle C is about $180° - (34° + 48°)$ or about $98°$.

Use the Law of Sines again to find c.
$$\frac{\sin 98°}{c} \approx \frac{\sin 34°}{6}$$
$$c \approx \frac{6 \sin 98°}{\sin 34°}$$
$$c \approx 10.6$$

Obtuse B

To find B you need to find an obtuse angle whose sine is also 0.7456.

To do this, subtract the angle given by your calculator, $48°$, from $180°$. So B is approximately $132°$.

The measure of angle C is about $180° - (34° + 132°)$ or about $14°$.

Use the Law of Sines to find c.
$$\frac{\sin 14°}{c} \approx \frac{\sin 34°}{6}$$
$$c \approx \frac{6 \sin 14°}{\sin 34°}$$
$$c \approx 2.6$$

Exercises

Determine whether each triangle has *no* solution, *one* solution, or *two* solutions. Then solve the triangle. Round side lengths to the nearest tenth and angle measures to the nearest degree.

1. $A = 50°$, $a = 34$, $b = 40$　　**2.** $A = 24°$, $a = 3$, $b = 8$　　**3.** $A = 125°$, $a = 22$, $b = 15$

13-4 Skills Practice

Law of Sines

Find the area of △ABC to the nearest tenth, if necessary.

1.

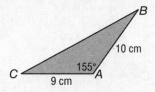

2.

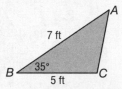

3. $A = 35°, b = 3$ ft, $c = 7$ ft

4. $C = 148°, a = 10$ cm, $b = 7$ cm

5. $C = 22°, a = 14$ m, $b = 8$ m

6. $B = 93°, c = 18$ mi, $a = 42$ mi

Solve each triangle. Round side lengths to the nearest tenth and angle measures to the nearest degree.

7.

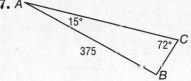

8.

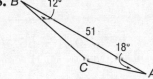

9.

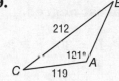

10.

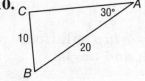

11.

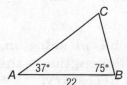

12.

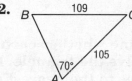

Determine whether each triangle has *no* solution, *one* solution, or *two* solutions. Then solve the triangle. Round side lengths to the nearest tenth and angle measures to the nearest degree.

13. $A = 30°, a = 1, b = 4$

14. $A = 30°, a = 2, b = 4$

15. $A = 30°, a = 3, b = 4$

16. $A = 38°, a = 10, b = 9$

17. $A = 78°, a = 8, b = 5$

18. $A = 133°, a = 9, b = 7$

19. $A = 127°, a = 2, b = 6$

20. $A = 109°, a = 24, b = 13$

Lesson 13-4

13-4 Practice

Law of Sines

Find the area of △ABC to the nearest tenth, if necessary.

1.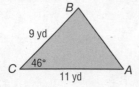

2.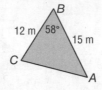

3.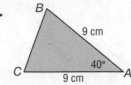

4. $C = 32°$, $a = 12.6$ m, $b = 8.9$ m

5. $B = 27°$, $a = 14.9$ cm, $c = 18.6$ cm

6. $A = 17.4°$, $b = 12$ km, $c = 14$ km

7. $A = 34°$, $b = 19.4$ ft, $c = 8.6$ ft

Solve each triangle. Round side lengths to the nearest tenth and angle measures to the nearest degree.

8. $A = 50°$, $B = 30°$, $c = 9$

9. $A = 56°$, $B = 38°$, $a = 12$

10. $A = 80°$, $C = 14°$, $a = 40$

11. $B = 47°$, $C = 112°$, $b = 13$

12. $A = 72°$, $a = 8$, $c = 6$

13. $A = 25°$, $C = 107°$, $b = 12$

Determine whether each triangle has *no* solution, *one* solution, or *two* solutions. Then solve the triangle. Round side lengths to the nearest tenth and angle measures to the nearest degree if necessary.

14. $A = 29°$, $a = 6$, $b = 13$

15. $A = 70°$, $a = 25$, $b = 20$

16. $A = 113°$, $a = 21$, $b = 25$

17. $A = 110°$, $a = 20$, $b = 8$

18. $A = 66°$, $a = 12$, $b = 7$

19. $A = 54°$, $a = 5$, $b = 8$

20. $A = 45°$, $a = 15$, $b = 18$

21. $A = 60°$, $a = 4\sqrt{3}$, $b = 8$

22. **WILDLIFE** Sarah Phillips, an officer for the Department of Fisheries and Wildlife, checks boaters on a lake to make sure they do not disturb two osprey nesting sites. She leaves a dock and heads due north in her boat to the first nesting site. From here, she turns 5° north of due west and travels an additional 2.14 miles to the second nesting site. She then travels 6.7 miles directly back to the dock. How far from the dock is the first osprey nesting site? Round to the nearest tenth.

13-4 Word Problem Practice

Law of Sines

1. WALKING Alliya is taking a walk along a straight road. She decides to leave the road, so she walks on a path that makes an angle of 35° with the road. After walking for 450 meters, she turns 75° and heads back towards the road.

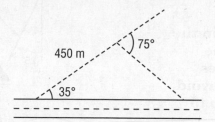

a. How far does Alliya need to walk on her current path to get back to the road?

b. When Alliya returns to the road, how far along the road is she from where she started?

2. SAILING A spinnaker is a large triangular sail that swings out opposite the mainsail, and is used when running with the wind. The *luff* is the leading edge of the sail, the *leach* is the edge away from the wind, and the *foot* is the bottom edge. Find the missing measure for each sail.

Luff (ft)	Leach (ft)	Foot (ft)	Angle between Luff and Leach	Area (ft²)
22	20	14	38°	
28	23.8	18		214.1
45		21	27°	357.5

3. FISHING A fishing pole is resting against the railing of a boat making an angle of 22° with the boat's deck. The fishing pole is 5 feet long, and the hook hangs 3 feet from the tip of the pole. The movement of the boat causes the hook to sway back and forth. Determine which angles the fishing line must make with the pole in order for the hook to be level with the boat's deck.

4. CAMERAS A security camera is located on top of a building at a certain distance from the sidewalk. The camera revolves counterclockwise at a steady rate of one revolution per minute. At one point in the revolution it directly faces a point on the sidewalk that is 20 meters from the camera. Four seconds later, it directly faces a point 10 meters down the sidewalk.

a. How many degrees does the camera rotate in 4 seconds?

b. To the nearest tenth of a meter, how far is the security camera from the sidewalk?

Lesson 13-4

13-4 Enrichment

Navigation

The bearing of a boat is an angle showing the direction the boat is heading. Often, the angle is measured from north, but it can be measured from any of the four compass directions. At the right, the bearing of the boat is 155°. Or, it can be described as 25° east of south (S25°E).

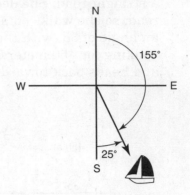

Example   A boat A sights the lighthouse B in the direction N65°E and the spire of a church C in the direction S75°E. According to the map, B is 7 miles from C in the direction N30°W. In order for A to avoid running aground, find the bearing it should keep to pass B at 4 miles distance.

In $\triangle ABC$, $\angle\alpha = 180° - 65° - 75°$ or $40°$
$$\angle C = 180° - 30° - (180° - 75°)$$
$$= 45°$$
$$a = 7 \text{ miles}$$

With the Law of Sines,

$$AB = \frac{a \sin C}{\sin \alpha} = \frac{7(\sin 45°)}{\sin 40°} = 7.7 \text{ mi.}$$

The ray for the correct bearing for A must be tangent at X to circle B with radius $BX = 4$. Thus $\triangle ABX$ is a right triangle.

Then $\sin \theta = \dfrac{BX}{AB} = \dfrac{4}{7.7} \approx 0.519$. Therefore, $\angle \theta = 31.3°$.

The bearing of A should be $65° - 31.3°$ or $33.7°$ east of north.

Exercises

1. Suppose the lighthouse B in the example is sighted at S30°W by a ship P due north of the church C. Find the bearing P should keep to pass B at 4 miles distance.

2. In the fog, the lighthouse keeper determines by radar that a boat 18 miles away is heading to the shore. The direction of the lighthouse from the boat is S80°E. What bearing should the lighthouse keeper radio the boat to take to come ashore 4 miles south of the lighthouse?

13-5 Study Guide and Intervention

Law of Cosines

Use Law of Cosines to Solve Triangles

Law of Cosines	Let $\triangle ABC$ be any triangle with a, b, and c representing the measures of the sides, and opposite angles with measures A, B, and C, respectively. Then the following equations are true. $$a^2 = b^2 + c^2 - 2bc \cos A$$ $$b^2 = a^2 + c^2 - 2ac \cos B$$ $$c^2 = a^2 + b^2 - 2ab \cos C$$

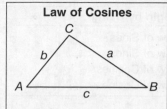

You can use the Law of Cosines to solve any triangle if you know the measures of two sides and the included angle (SAS case), or the measures of three sides (SSS case).

Example **Solve $\triangle ABC$.**

You are given the measures of two sides and the included angle.
Begin by using the Law of Cosines to determine c.

$c^2 = a^2 + b^2 - 2ab \cos C$

$c^2 = 28^2 + 15^2 - 2(28)(15)\cos 82°$

$c^2 \approx 892.00$

$c \approx 29.9$

Next you can use the Law of Sines to find the measure of angle A.

$\dfrac{\sin A}{a} = \dfrac{\sin C}{c}$

$\dfrac{\sin A}{28} \approx \dfrac{\sin 82°}{29.9}$

$\sin A \approx 0.9273$

$A \approx 68°$

The measure of B is about $180° - (82° + 68°)$ or about $30°$.

Exercises

Solve each triangle. Round side lengths to the nearest tenth and angle measures to the nearest degree.

1. $a = 14$, $c = 20$, $B = 38°$

2. $A = 60°$, $c = 17$, $b = 12$

3. $a = 4$, $b = 6$, $c = 3$

4. $A = 103°$, $b = 31$, $c = 52$

5. $a = 15$, $b = 26$, $C = 132°$

6. $a = 31$, $b = 52$, $c = 43$

Lesson 13-5

13-5　Study Guide and Intervention　(continued)

Law of Cosines

Choose a Method to Solve Triangles

	Given	Begin by Using
Solving an Oblique Triangle	two angles and any side	Law of Sines
	two sides and an angle opposite one of them	Law of Sines
	two sides and their included angle	Law of Cosines
	three sides	Law of Cosines

Example　**Determine whether $\triangle ABC$ should be solved by beginning with the Law of *Sines* or Law of *Cosines*. Then solve the triangle.**

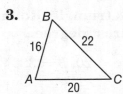

You are given the measures of two sides and their included angle, so use the Law of Cosines.

$a^2 = b^2 + c^2 - 2bc \cos A$　　　Law of Cosines

$a^2 = 20^2 + 8^2 - 2(20)(8) \cos 34°$　　$b = 20, c = 8, A = 34°$

$a^2 \approx 198.71$　　　Use a calculator to simplify.

$a \approx 14.1$　　　Use a calculator to simplify.

Use the Law of Sines to find C.

$\dfrac{\sin C}{c} = \dfrac{\sin A}{a}$　　　Law of Sines

$\sin C \approx \dfrac{8 \sin 34°}{14.1}$　　$c = 8, A = 34°, a \approx 14.1$

$C \approx 18°$　　　Use the $\sin^{-1}$ function.

The measure of angle B is approximately $180° - (34° + 18°)$ or about $128°$.

Exercises

Determine whether each triangle should be solved by beginning with the Law of *Sines* or Law of *Cosines*. Then solve the triangle.

1.
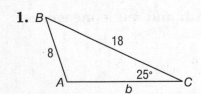

2.
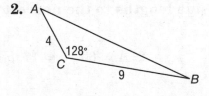

3.
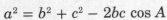

4. $A = 58°, a = 12, b = 8$　　　**5.** $a = 28, b = 35, c = 20$　　　**6.** $A = 82°, B = 44°, b = 11$

13-5 Skills Practice

Law of Cosines

Solve each triangle. Round side lengths to the nearest tenth and angle measures to the nearest degree.

1.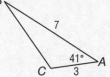

2.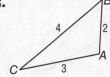

3.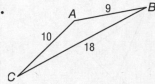

4. $C = 71°, a = 3, b = 4$

5. $C = 35°, a = 5, b = 8$

Determine whether each triangle should be solved by begining with the Law of *Sines* or the Law of *Cosines*. Then solve the triangle.

6.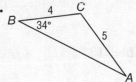

7.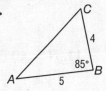

8.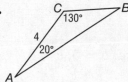

9. $A = 11°, C = 27°, c = 50$

10. $B = 47°, a = 20, c = 24$

11. $A = 71°, C = 62°, a = 20$

12. $a = 5, b = 12, c = 13$

13. $A = 51°, b = 7, c = 10$

14. $a = 13, A = 41°, B = 75°$

15. $B = 125°, a = 8, b = 14$

16. $a = 5, b = 6, c = 7$

Lesson 13-5

13-5 Practice

Law of Cosines

Determine whether each triangle should be solved by beginning with the Law of *Sines* or Law of *Cosines*. Then solve the triangle.

1.

2.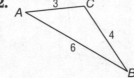

3.

4. $a = 16, b = 20, C = 54°$

5. $B = 71°, c = 6, a = 11$

6. $A = 37°, a = 20, b = 18$

7. $C = 35°, a = 18, b = 24$

8. $a = 8, b = 6, c = 9$

9. $A = 23°, b = 10, c = 12$

10. $a = 4, b = 5, c = 8$

11. $B = 46.6°, C = 112°, b = 13$

12. $A = 46.3°, a = 35, b = 30$

13. $a = 16.4, b = 21.1, c = 18.5$

14. $C = 43.5°, b = 8, c = 6$

15. $A = 78.3°, b = 7, c = 11$

16. SATELLITES Two radar stations 2.4 miles apart are tracking an airplane. The straight-line distance between Station A and the plane is 7.4 miles. The straight-line distance between Station B and the plane is 6.9 miles. What is the angle of elevation from Station A to the plane? Round to the nearest degree.

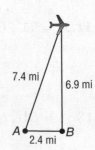

17. DRAFTING Marion is using a computer-aided drafting program to produce a drawing for a client. She begins a triangle by drawing a segment 4.2 inches long from point A to point B. From B, she draws a second segment that forms a 42 angle with $\overline{AB}$ and is 6.4 inches long, ending at point C. To the nearest tenth, how long is the segment from C to A?

13-5 Word Problem Practice

Law of Cosines

1. POOLS The Perth County pool has a lifeguard station in both the deep water and shallow water sections of the pool. The distance between each station and the bottom of the slide is known, but the manager would like to calculate more information about the pool setup.

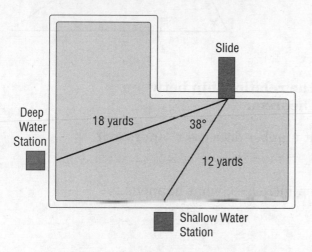

a. When the lifeguards switch positions, the lifeguard at the deep water station swims to the shallow water station. How far does the lifeguard swim?

b. If the lifeguard at the deepwater station is directly facing the bottom of the slide, what angle does she need to turn in order to face the lifeguard at the shallow water station?

2. CAMPING At Shady Pines Campground, Campsites A and B are situated 80 meters apart. The camp office is 95 meters from Campsite A and 115 meters from Campsite B. When the ranger is standing at the office, what is the angle of separation between Campsites A and B?

3. SKATING During a figure skating routine, Jackie and Peter skate apart with an angle of 15° between them. Jackie skates for 5 meters and Peter skates for 7 meters. How far apart are the skaters?

4. TECHNOLOGY Gina's handheld PDA can send and receive e-mails if it is within 40 miles of a transmission tower. On a trip, Gina drives past the transmission tower on Highway 7 for 32 miles, and then she turns onto Oakville Road and drives for another 19 miles.

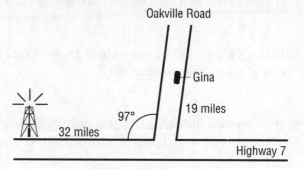

a. Is Gina close enough to the transmission tower to be able to send and receive e-mails? Explain your reasoning.

b. If Gina is within range of the tower, how much farther can she drive on Oakville Road before she is out of range? If she is out of range and drives back towards Highway 7, how far will she travel before she is back in range?

Lesson 13-5

13-5 Enrichment

The Law of Cosines and the Pythagorean Theorem

The Law of Cosines bears strong similarities to the
Pythagorean Theorem. According to the Law of Cosines,
if two sides of a triangle have lengths a and b and if
the angle between them has a measure of $x°$, then the
length, y, of the third side of the triangle can be found
by using the equation

$$y^2 = a^2 + b^2 - 2ab \cos x°.$$

**Answer the following questions to clarify the relationship between
the Law of Cosines and the Pythagorean Theorem.**

1. If the value of $x°$ becomes less and less, what number does $\cos x°$ approach?

2. If the value of $x°$ is very close to zero but then increases, what happens to
$\cos x°$ as $x°$ approaches 90°?

3. If $x°$ equals 90°, what is the value of $\cos x°$? What does the equation of
$y^2 = a^2 + b^2 - 2ab \cos x°$ simplify to if $x°$ equals 90°?

4. What happens to the value of $\cos x°$ as $x°$ increases beyond 90° and
approaches 180°?

5. Consider some particular value of a and b, say 7 for a and 19 for b. Use a
graphing calculator to graph the equation you get by solving
$y^2 = 7^2 + 19^2 - 2(7)(19) \cos x°$ for y.

a. In view of the geometry of the situation, what range of values should
you use for $x°$?

b. Display the graph and use the TRACE function. What do the maximum
and minimum values appear to be for the function?

c. How do the answers for part b relate to the lengths 7 and 19? Are the
maximum and minimum values from part b ever actually attained in
the geometric situation?

13-6 Study Guide and Intervention

Circular Functions

Circular Functions

Definition of Sine and Cosine	If the terminal side of an angle θ in standard position intersects the unit circle at $P(x, y)$, then $\cos \theta = x$ and $\sin \theta = y$. Therefore, the coordinates of P can be written as $P(\cos \theta, \sin \theta)$.	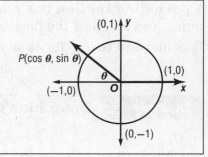

Example The terminal side of angle θ in standard position intersects the unit circle at $P\left(-\dfrac{5}{6}, \dfrac{\sqrt{11}}{6}\right)$. Find $\cos \theta$ and $\sin \theta$.

$P\left(-\dfrac{5}{6}, \dfrac{\sqrt{11}}{6}\right) = P(\cos \theta, \sin \theta)$, so $\cos \theta = -\dfrac{5}{6}$ and $\sin \theta = \dfrac{\sqrt{11}}{6}$.

Exercises

The terminal side of angle θ in standard position intersects the unit circle at each point P. Find $\cos \theta$ and $\sin \theta$.

1. $P\left(-\dfrac{\sqrt{3}}{2}, \dfrac{1}{2}\right)$

2. $P(0, -1)$

3. $P\left(-\dfrac{2}{3}, \dfrac{\sqrt{5}}{3}\right)$

4. $P\left(-\dfrac{4}{5}, -\dfrac{3}{5}\right)$

5. $P\left(\dfrac{1}{6}, -\dfrac{\sqrt{35}}{6}\right)$

6. $P\left(\dfrac{\sqrt{7}}{4}, \dfrac{3}{4}\right)$

7. P is on the terminal side of $\theta = 45°$.

8. P is on the terminal side of $\theta = 120°$.

9. P is on the terminal side of $\theta = 240°$.

10. P is on the terminal side of $\theta = 330°$.

Lesson 13-5

13-6 Study Guide and Intervention (continued)

Circular Functions

Periodic Functions

A **periodic function** has y-values that repeat at regular intervals. One complete pattern is called a **cycle**, and the horizontal length of one cycle is called a **period**.

The sine and cosine functions are periodic; each has a period of 360° or 2π radians.

Example 1 **Determine the period of the function.**

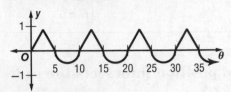

The pattern of the function repeats every 10 units, so the period of the function is 10.

Example 2 **Find the exact value of each function.**

a. $\sin 855°$

$\sin 855° = \sin (135° + 720°)$

$\quad\quad\quad = \sin 135°$ or $\dfrac{\sqrt{2}}{2}$

b. $\cos \left(\dfrac{31\pi}{6}\right)$

$\cos \left(\dfrac{31\pi}{6}\right) = \cos \left(\dfrac{7\pi}{6} + 4\pi\right)$

$\quad\quad\quad\quad = \cos \dfrac{7\pi}{6}$ or $-\dfrac{\sqrt{3}}{2}$

Exercises

Determine the period of each function.

1.

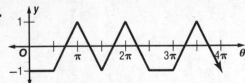

2.

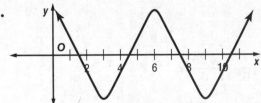

Find the exact value of each function.

3. $\sin (-510°)$

4. $\sin 495°$

5. $\cos \left(-\dfrac{5\pi}{2}\right)$

6. $\sin \left(\dfrac{5\pi}{3}\right)$

7. $\cos \left(\dfrac{11\pi}{4}\right)$

8. $\sin \left(-\dfrac{3\pi}{4}\right)$

13-6 Skill Practice

Circular Functions

The terminal side of angle θ in standard position intersects the unit circle at each point P. Find $\cos \theta$ and $\sin \theta$.

1. $P\left(\dfrac{3}{5}, \dfrac{4}{5}\right)$

2. $P\left(\dfrac{5}{13}, -\dfrac{12}{13}\right)$

3. $P\left(-\dfrac{9}{41}, -\dfrac{40}{41}\right)$

4. $P(0, 1)$

5. $P(-1, 0)$

6. $P\left(\dfrac{1}{2}, -\dfrac{\sqrt{3}}{2}\right)$

Find the exact value of each function.

7. $\cos 45°$

8. $\sin 210°$

9. $\sin 330°$

10. $\cos 330°$

11. $\cos (-60°)$

12. $\sin (-390°)$

13. $\sin 5\pi$

14. $\cos 3\pi$

15. $\sin \dfrac{5\pi}{2}$

16. $\sin \dfrac{7\pi}{3}$

17. $\cos \left(-\dfrac{7\pi}{3}\right)$

18. $\cos \left(-\dfrac{5\pi}{6}\right)$

Determine the period of each function.

19.

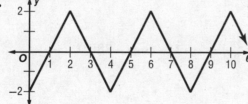

20.

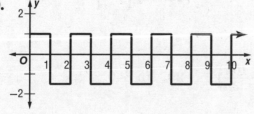

21.

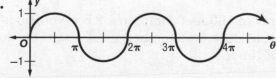

Lesson 13-6

13-6 Practice

Circular Functions

The terminal side of angle θ in standard position intersects the unit circle at each point P. Find $\cos \theta$ and $\sin \theta$.

1. $P\left(-\dfrac{1}{2}, \dfrac{\sqrt{3}}{2}\right)$

2. $P\left(\dfrac{20}{29}, -\dfrac{21}{29}\right)$

3. $P(0.8, 0.6)$

4. $P(0, -1)$

5. $P\left(-\dfrac{\sqrt{2}}{2}, -\dfrac{\sqrt{2}}{2}\right)$

6. $P\left(\dfrac{\sqrt{3}}{2}, \dfrac{1}{2}\right)$

Determine the period of each function.

7.

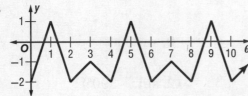

8.

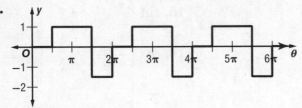

Find the exact value of each function.

9. $\cos \dfrac{7\pi}{4}$

10. $\sin (-30°)$

11. $\sin \left(-\dfrac{2\pi}{3}\right)$

12. $\cos (-330°)$

13. $\cos 600°$

14. $\sin \dfrac{9\pi}{2}$

15. $\cos 7\pi$

16. $\cos \left(-\dfrac{11\pi}{4}\right)$

17. $\sin (-225°)$

18. $\sin 585°$

19. $\cos \left(-\dfrac{10\pi}{3}\right)$

20. $\sin 840°$

21. FERRIS WHEELS A Ferris wheel with a diameter of 100 feet completes 2.5 revolutions per minute. What is the period of the function that describes the height of a seat on the outside edge of the Ferris wheel as a function of time?

13-6 Word Problem Practice

Circular Functions

Lesson 13-6

1. TIRES A point on the edge of a car tire is marked with paint. As the car moves slowly, the marked point on the tire varies in distance from the surface of the road. The height in inches of the point is given by the expression $h = -8\cos t + 8$, where t is the time in seconds.

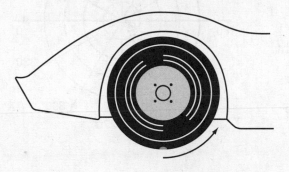

a. What is the maximum height above ground that the point on the tire reaches?

b. What is the minimum height above ground that the point on the tire reaches?

c. How many rotations does the tire make per second?

d. How far does the marked point travel in 30 seconds? How far does the marked point travel in one hour?

2. GEOMETRY The temperature T in degrees Fahrenheit of a city t months into the year is approximated by the formula $T = 42 + 30 \sin\left(\frac{\pi}{6}t\right)$.

a. What is the highest monthly temperature for the city?

b. In what month does the highest temperature occur?

c. What is the lowest monthly temperature for the city?

d. In what month does the lowest temperature occur?

3. THE MOON The Moon's period of revolution is the number of days it takes for the Moon to revolve around Earth. The period can be determined by graphing the percentage of sunlight reflected by the Moon each day, as seen by an observer on Earth. Use the graph to determine the Moon's period of revolution.

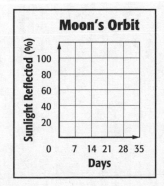

13-6 Enrichment

Polar Coordinates

Consider an angle in standard position with its vertex at a point O called the *pole*. Its initial side is on a coordinated axis called the *polar axis*. A point P on the terminal side of the angle is named by the *polar coordinates* (r, θ) where r is the directed distance of the point from O and θ is the measure of the angle.

Graphs in this system may be drawn on polar coordinate paper such as the kind shown at the right.

The polar coordinates of a point are not unique. For example, $(3, 30°)$ names point P as well as $(3, 390°)$. Another name for P is $(-3, 210°)$. Can you see why? The coordinates of the pole are $(0, \theta)$ where θ may be any angle.

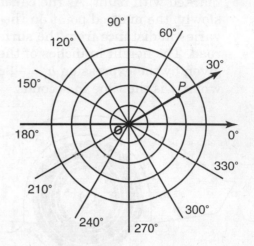

Example Draw the graph of the function $r = \cos \theta$. Make a table of convenient values for θ and r. Then plot the points.

θ	0°	30°	60°	90°	120°	150°	180°
r	1	$\frac{\sqrt{3}}{2}$	$\frac{1}{2}$	0	$-\frac{1}{2}$	$-\frac{\sqrt{3}}{2}$	-1

Since the period of the cosine function is 180°, values of r for $\theta > 180°$ are repeated.

Graph each function by making a table of values and plotting the values on polar coordinate paper.

1. $r = 4$

2. $r = 3 \sin \theta$

3. $r = 3 \cos 2\theta$

4. $r = 2(1 + \cos \theta)$

13-7 Study Guide and Intervention

Graphing Trigonometric Functions

Sine, Cosine, and Tangent Functions Trigonometric functions can be graphed on the coordinate plane. Graphs of periodic functions have repeating patterns, or *cycles*; the horizontal length of each cycle is the *period*. The **amplitude** of the graph of a sine or cosine function equals half the difference between the maximum and minimum values of the function. Tangent is a trigonometric function that has asymptotes when graphed.

	Parent Function	$y = \sin\theta$	$y = \cos\theta$	$y = \tan\theta$
Sine, Cosine, and Tangent Functions	Domain	{all real numbers}	{all real numbers}	$\{\theta \mid \theta \neq 90 + 180n, n \text{ is an integer}\}$
	Range	$\{y \mid -1 \leq y \leq 1\}$	$\{y \mid -1 \leq y \leq 1\}$	{all real numbers}
	Amplitude	1	1	undefined
	Period	360°	360°	180°

Lesson 13-7

Example Find the amplitude and period of each function. Then graph the function.

a. $y = 4\cos\dfrac{\theta}{3}$

First, find the amplitude.

$|a| = |4|$, so the amplitude is 4.

Next find the period.

$\dfrac{360°}{\left|\frac{1}{3}\right|} = 1080°$

Use the amplitude and period to help graph the function.

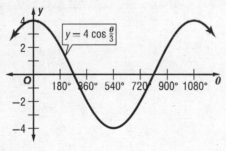

b. $y = \dfrac{1}{2}\tan 2\theta$

The amplitude is not defined, and the period is 90°.

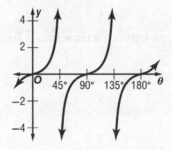

Exercises

Find the amplitude, if it exists, and period of each function. Then graph the function.

1. $y = -4\sin\theta$

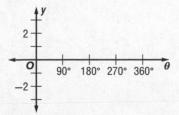

2. $y = 2\tan\dfrac{\theta}{2}$

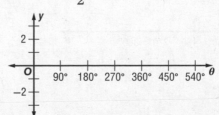

13-7 Study Guide and Intervention *(continued)*

Graphing Trigonometric Functions

Graphs of Other Trigonometric Functions The graphs of the cosecant, secant, and cotangent functions are related to the graphs of the sine, cosine, and tangent functions.

	Parent Function	$y = \csc \theta$	$y = \sec \theta$	$y = \cot \theta$
Cosecant, Secant, and Cotangent Functions	Domain	$\{\theta \mid \theta \neq 180n, n$ is an integer$\}$	$\{\theta \mid \theta \neq 90 + 180n, n$ is an integer$\}$	$\{\theta \mid \theta \neq 180n, n$ is an integer$\}$
	Range	$\{y \mid -1 > y$ or $y > 1\}$	$\{y \mid -1 > y$ or $y > 1\}$	$\{$all real numbers$\}$
	Amplitude	undefined	undefined	undefined
	Period	360°	360°	180°

Example Find the period of $y = \frac{1}{2} \csc \theta$. Then graph the function.

Since $\frac{1}{2} \csc \theta$ is a reciprocal of $\frac{1}{2} \sin \theta$, the graphs have the same period, 360°. The vertical asymptotes occur at the points where $\frac{1}{2} \sin \theta = 0$. So, the asymptotes are at $\theta = 0°$, $\theta = 180°$, and $\theta = 360°$. Sketch $y = \frac{1}{2} \sin \theta$ and use it to graph $y = \frac{1}{2} \csc \theta$.

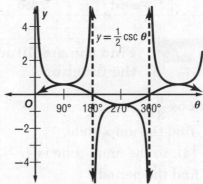

Exercises

Find the period of each function. Then graph the function.

1. $y = \cot 2\theta$

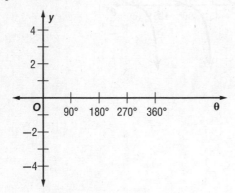

2. $y = \sec 3\theta$

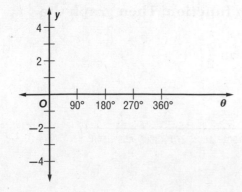

13-7 Skills Practice

Graphing Trigonometric Functions

Find the amplitude and period of each function. Then graph the function.

1. $y = 2 \cos \theta$

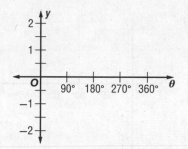

2. $y = 4 \sin \theta$

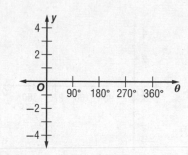

3. $y = 2 \sec \theta$

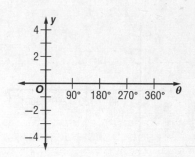

4. $y = \frac{1}{2} \tan \theta$

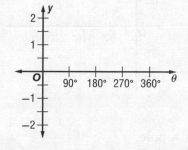

5. $y = \sin 3\theta$

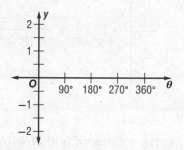

6. $y = \csc 3\theta$

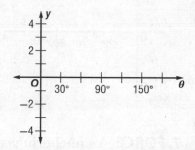

7. $y = \tan 2\theta$

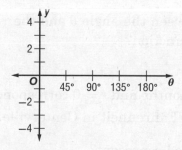

8. $y = \cos 2\theta$

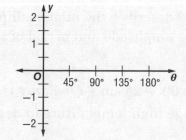

9. $y = 4 \sin \frac{1}{2}\theta$

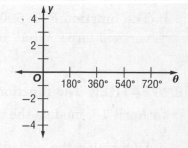

Lesson 13-7

13-7 Practice

Graphing Trigonometric Functions

Find the amplitude, if it exists, and period of each function. Then graph the function.

1. $y = -4 \sin \theta$

2. $y = \cot \frac{1}{2}\theta$

3. $y = \cos 5\theta$

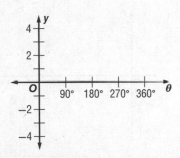

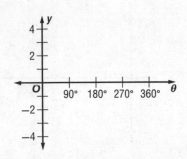

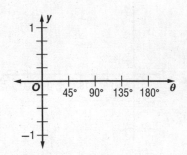

4. $y = \csc \frac{3}{4}\theta$

5. $y = 2 \tan \frac{1}{2}\theta$

6. $y = \frac{1}{2} \sin \theta$

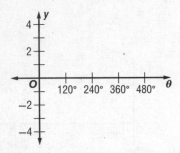

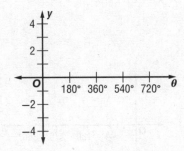

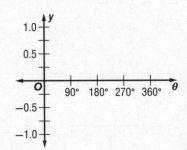

7. FORCE An anchoring cable exerts a force of 500 Newtons on a pole. The force has the horizontal and vertical components F_x and F_y. (A force of one Newton (N), is the force that gives an acceleration of 1 m/sec² to a mass of 1 kg.)

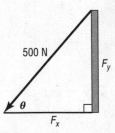

  a. The function $F_x = 500 \cos \theta$ describes the relationship between the angle θ and the horizontal force. What are the amplitude and period of this function?

  b. The function $F_y = 500 \sin \theta$ describes the relationship between the angle θ and the vertical force. What are the amplitude and period of this function?

8. WEATHER The function $y = 60 + 25 \sin \frac{\pi}{6}t$, where t is in months and $t = 0$ corresponds to April 15, models the average high temperature in degrees Fahrenheit in Centerville.

  a. Determine the period of this function. What does this period represent?

  b. What is the maximum high temperature and when does this occur?

13-7 Word Problem Practice

Graphing Trigonometric Functions

1. PHYSICS The following chart gives functions which model the wave patterns of different colors of light emitted from a particular source, where y is the height of the wave in nanometers and t is the length from the start of the wave in nanometers.

Color	Function
Red	$y = 300 \sin\left(\frac{\pi}{350}t\right)$
Orange	$y = 125 \sin\left(\frac{\pi}{305}t\right)$
Yellow	$y = 460 \sin\left(\frac{\pi}{290}t\right)$
Green	$y = 200 \sin\left(\frac{\pi}{260}t\right)$
Blue	$y = 40 \sin\left(\frac{\pi}{235}t\right)$
Violet	$y = 80 \sin\left(\frac{\pi}{210}t\right)$

a. What are the amplitude and period of the function describing green light waves?

b. The intensity of a light wave corresponds directly to its amplitude. Which color emitted from the source is the most intense?

c. The color of light depends on the period of the wave. Which color has the shortest period? The longest period?

2. SWIMMING As Charles swims a 25 meter sprint, the position of his right hand relative to the water surface can be modeled by the graph below, where g is the height of the hand in inches from the water level and t is the time in seconds past the start of the sprint. What function describes this graph?

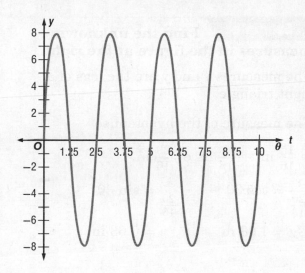

3. ENVIRONMENT In a certain forest, the leaf density can be modeled by the equation $y = 20 + 15 \sin\left(\frac{\pi}{6}(t - 3)\right)$ where y represents the number of leaves per square foot and t represents the month where January = 1.

a. Determine the period of this function. What does this period represent?

b. What is the maximum leaf density that occurs in this forest and when does this occur?

13-7 Enrichment

Blueprints

Interpreting blueprints requires the ability to select and use trigonometric functions and geometric properties. The figure below represents a plan for an improvement to a roof. The metal fitting shown makes a 30° angle with the horizontal. The vertices of the geometric shapes are *not* labeled in these plans. Relevant information must be selected and the appropriate function used to find the unknown measures.

Example Find the unknown measures in the figure at the right.

The measures x and y are the legs of a right triangle.

The measure of the hypotenuse

is $\frac{15}{16}$ in. + $\frac{5}{16}$ in. or $\frac{20}{16}$ in.

$\dfrac{y}{\frac{20}{16}} = \cos 30°$ $\dfrac{x}{\frac{20}{16}} = \sin 30°$

$y = 1.08$ in. $x = 0.63$ in.

Roofing Improvement

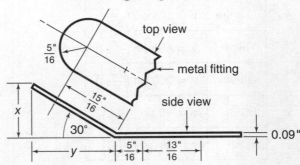

Find the unknown measures of each of the following. Assume that all angles that appear to be right angles are right angles.

1. Chimney on roof

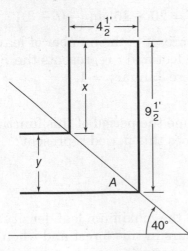

2. Air vent

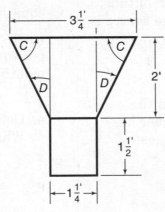

3. Elbow joint

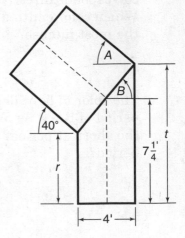

13-8　Study Guide and Intervention

Translations of Trigonometric Graphs

Horizontal Translations When a constant is subtracted from the angle measure in a trigonometric function, a **phase shift** of the graph results.

Phase Shift	The phase shift of the graphs of the functions $y = a \sin b(\theta - h)$, $y = a \cos b(\theta - h)$, and $y = a \tan b(\theta - h)$ is h, where $b > 0$. If $h > 0$, the shift is h units to the right. If $h < 0$, the shift is h units to the left.

Example　State the amplitude, period, and phase shift for $y = \frac{1}{2} \cos 3\left(\theta - \frac{\pi}{2}\right)$. Then graph the function.

Amplitude: $|a| = \left|\frac{1}{2}\right|$ or $\frac{1}{2}$

Period: $\frac{2\pi}{|b|} = \frac{2\pi}{|3|}$ or $\frac{2\pi}{3}$

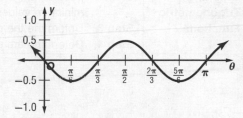

Phase Shift: $h = \frac{\pi}{2}$

The phase shift is to the right since $\frac{\pi}{2} > 0$.

Exercises

State the amplitude, period, and phase shift for each function. Then graph the function.

1. $y = 2 \sin (\theta + 60°)$

2. $y = \tan \left(\theta - \frac{\pi}{2}\right)$

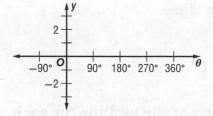

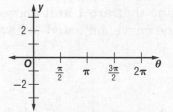

3. $y = 3 \cos (\theta - 45°)$

4. $y = \frac{1}{2} \sin 3\left(\theta - \frac{\pi}{3}\right)$

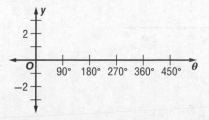

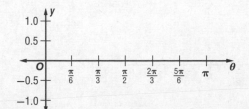

Lesson 13-8

13-8 Study Guide and Intervention *(continued)*

Translations of Trigonometric Graphs

Vertical Translations When a constant is added to a trigonometric function, the graph is shifted vertically.

Vertical Shift	The vertical shift of the graphs of the functions $y = a \sin b(\theta - h) + k$, $y = a \cos b(\theta - h) + k$, and $y = a \tan b(\theta - h) + k$ is k. If $k > 0$, the shift is k units up. If $k < 0$, the shift is k units down.

The **midline** of a vertical shift is $y = k$.

Graphing Trigonometric Functions	Step 1	Determine the vertical shift, and graph the midline.
	Step 2	Determine the amplitude, if it exists. Use dashed lines to indicate the maximum and minimum values of the function.
	Step 3	Determine the period of the function and graph the appropriate function.
	Step 4	Determine the phase shift and translate the graph accordingly.

Example State the amplitude, period, vertical shift, and equation of the midline for $y = \cos 2\theta - 3$. Then graph the function.

Amplitude: $|a| = |1|$ or 1

Period: $\dfrac{2\pi}{|b|} = \dfrac{2\pi}{|2|}$ or π

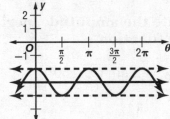

Vertical Shift: $k = -3$, so the vertical shift is 3 units down.

The equation of the midline is $y = -3$.

Since the amplitude of the function is 1, draw dashed lines parallel to the midline that are 1 unit above and below the midline. Then draw the cosine curve, adjusted to have a period of π.

Exercises

State the amplitude, period, vertical shift, and equation of the midline for each function. Then graph the function.

1. $y = \dfrac{1}{2} \cos \theta + 2$ 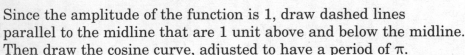 **2.** $y = 3 \sin \theta - 2$

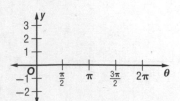

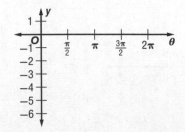

13-8 Skills Practice

Translations of Trigonometric Graphs

State the amplitude, period, and phase shift for each function. Then graph the function.

1. $y = \sin(\theta + 90°)$

2. $y = \cos(\theta - 45°)$

3. $y = \tan\left(\theta - \dfrac{\pi}{2}\right)$

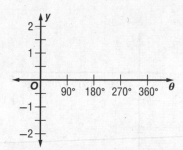
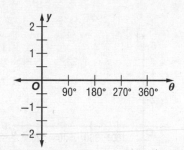
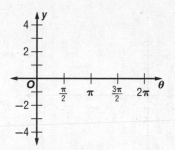

State the amplitude, period, vertical shift, and equation of the midline for each function. Then graph the function.

4. $y = \csc\theta - 2$

5. $y = \cos\theta + 1$

6. $y = \sec\theta + 3$

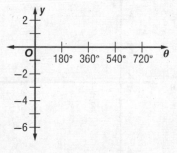
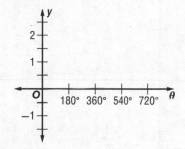
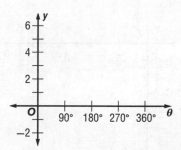

State the amplitude, period, phase shift, and vertical shift of each function. Then graph the function.

7. $y = 2\cos[3(\theta + 45°)] + 2$

8. $y = 3\sin[2(\theta - 90°)] + 2$

9. $y = 4\cot\left[\dfrac{4}{3}\left(\theta + \dfrac{\pi}{4}\right)\right] - 2$

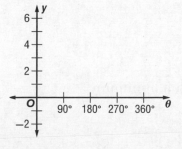
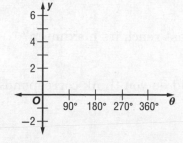
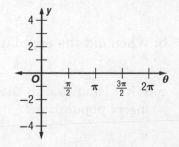

Lesson 13-8

13-8 Practice

Translations of Trigonometric Graphs

State the amplitude, period, phase shift, and vertical shift for each function. Then graph the function.

1. $y = \frac{1}{2} \tan \left(\theta - \frac{\pi}{2}\right)$

2. $y = 2 \cos (\theta + 30°) + 3$

3. $y = 3 \csc (2\theta + 60°) - 2.5$

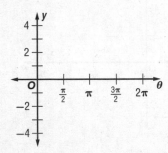

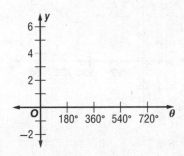

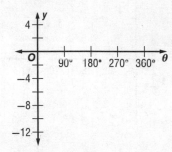

4. $y = -3 + 2 \sin 2\left(\theta + \frac{\pi}{4}\right)$

5. $y = 3 \cos 2 (\theta + 45°) + 1$

6. $y = -1 + 4 \tan (\theta + \pi)$

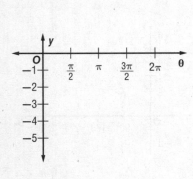

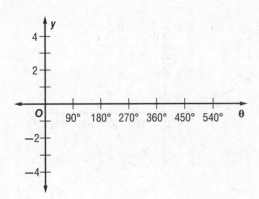

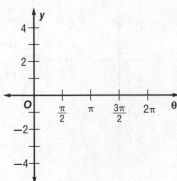

7. ECOLOGY The population of an insect species in a stand of trees follows the growth cycle of a particular tree species. The insect population can be modeled by the function $y = 40 + 30 \sin 6t$, where t is the number of years since the stand was first cut in November, 1920.

a. How often does the insect population reach its maximum level?

b. When did the population last reach its maximum?

c. What condition in the stand do you think corresponds with a minimum insect population?

13-8 Word Problem Practice

Translations of Trigonometric Graphs

1. CLOCKS A town hall has a tower with a clock on its face. The center of the clock is 40 feet above street level. The minute hand of the clock has a length of four feet.

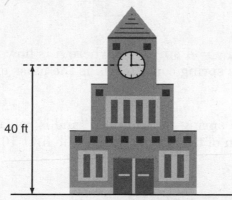

a. What is the maximum height of the tip of the minute hand above street level?

b. What is the minimum height of the tip of the minute hand above street level?

c. Write a sine function that represents the height above street level of the tip of the minute hand for t minutes after midnight.

d. Graph the function from your answer to part c.

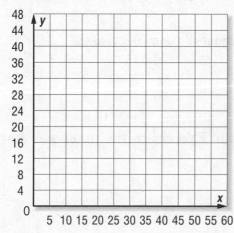

2. ANIMAL POPULATION The population of predators and prey in a closed ecological system tends to vary periodically over time. In a certain system, the population of snakes S can be represented by $S = 100 + 20 \sin\left(\frac{\pi}{5}t\right)$, where t is the number of years since January 1, 2000. In that same system, the population of rats can be represented by $R = 200 + 75 \sin\left(\frac{\pi}{5}t + \frac{\pi}{10}\right)$.

a. What is the maximum snake population?

b. When is this population first reached?

c. What is the minimum rat population?

d. When is this population first reached?

Lesson 13-8

13-8 Enrichment

Simple Harmonic Motion

Suppose a small object is attached to the end of a spring and then released. The object oscillates up and down in a periodic fashion. The motion of the object is known as simple harmonic motion.

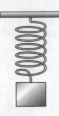

The motion of the object is described by the expression $y = A \sin \sqrt{\frac{k}{m}}\, t$, where A is how far down the object is pulled to stretch the spring, k is the spring constant, m is the mass of the object in grams, and t is the time in seconds.

1. A 10-gram object is attached to a spring that has a spring constant of 7, and is released after being pulled down 5 inches. Graph the motion of the spring during the first 10 seconds after the object is dropped.

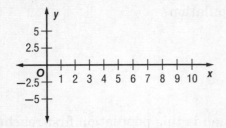

2. How many seconds does it take the object to complete one full oscillation?

3. How does the graph in Exercise 1 change as k increases? As k decreases?

4. How does the graph in Exercise 1 change as m increases? As m decreases?

5. Suppose that while timing the motion of the spring in Exercise 1, the timer was started 1 second early. How would this affect the graph?

13-9 Study Guide and Intervention

Inverse Trigonometric Functions

Inverse Trigonometric Functions If you know the value of a trigonometric function for an angle, you can use the *inverse* to find the angle. If you restrict the function's domain, then the inverse is a function. The values in this restricted domain are called **principal values**.

Principal Values of Sine, Cosine, and Tangent	$y = \text{Sin } x$ if and only if $y = \sin x$ and $-\frac{\pi}{2} \le x \le \frac{\pi}{2}$. $y = \text{Cos } x$ if and only if $y = \cos x$ and $0 \le x \le \pi$. $y = \text{Tan } x$ if and only if $y = \tan x$ and $-\frac{\pi}{2} \le x \le \frac{\pi}{2}$.
Inverse Sine, Cosine, and Tangent	Given $y = \text{Sin } x$, the inverse sine function is defined by $y = \text{Sin}^{-1} x$ or $y = \text{Arcsin } x$. Given $y = \text{Cos } x$, the inverse cosine function is defined by $y = \text{Cos}^{-1} x$ or $y = \text{Arccos } x$. Given $y = \text{Tan } x$, the inverse tangent function is given by $y = \text{Tan}^{-1} x$ or $y = \text{Arctan } x$.

Example 1 Find the value of $\text{Sin}^{-1}\left(\frac{\sqrt{3}}{2}\right)$. Write angle measures in degrees and radians.

Find the angle θ for $-\frac{\pi}{2} \le \theta \le \frac{\pi}{2}$ that has a sine value of $\frac{\sqrt{3}}{2}$.

Using a unit circle, the point on the circle that has y-coordinate of $\frac{\sqrt{3}}{2}$ is $\frac{\pi}{3}$ or $60°$.

So, $\text{Sin}^{-1}\left(\frac{\sqrt{3}}{2}\right) = \frac{\pi}{3}$ or $60°$.

Example 2 Find $\tan\left(\text{Sin}^{-1}\frac{1}{2}\right)$. Round to the nearest hundredth.

Let $\theta = \text{Sin}^{-1}\frac{1}{2}$. Then $\text{Sin } \theta = \frac{1}{2}$ with $-\frac{\pi}{2} < \theta < \frac{\pi}{2}$. The value $\theta = \frac{\pi}{6}$ satisfies both conditions. $\tan\frac{\pi}{6} = \frac{\sqrt{3}}{3}$ so $\tan\left(\text{Sin}^{-1}\frac{1}{2}\right) = \frac{\sqrt{3}}{3}$.

Exercises

Find each value. Write angle measures in degrees and radians.

1. $\text{Cos}^{-1}\left(\frac{\sqrt{3}}{2}\right)$

2. $\text{Sin}^{-1}\left(-\frac{\sqrt{3}}{2}\right)$

3. $\text{Arccos}\left(-\frac{1}{2}\right)$

4. $\text{Arctan } \sqrt{3}$

5. $\text{Arccos}\left(-\frac{\sqrt{2}}{2}\right)$

6. $\text{Tan}^{-1}(-1)$

Find each value. Round to the nearest hundredth if necessary.

7. $\cos\left[\text{Sin}^{-1}\left(-\frac{\sqrt{2}}{2}\right)\right]$

8. $\tan\left[\text{Arcsin}\left(-\frac{5}{7}\right)\right]$

9. $\sin\left(\text{Tan}^{-1}\frac{5}{12}\right)$

10. $\text{Cos}[\text{Arcsin}(-0.7)]$

11. $\cos(\text{Arctan } 5)$

12. $\sin(\text{Cos}^{-1} 0.3)$

Lesson 13-9

13-9   Study Guide and Intervention   (continued)

Inverse Trigonometric Functions

Solve Equations by Using Inverses You can rewrite trigonometric equations to solve for the measure of an angle.

Example   Solve the equation Sin $\theta = -0.25$. Round to the nearest tenth if necessary.

The sine of angle θ is -0.25. This can be written as Arcsin$(-0.25) = \theta$.

Use a calculator to solve.

KEYSTROKES: [2nd] [SIN⁻¹] [(−)] .25 [ENTER] −14.47751219

So, $\theta \approx -14.5°$

Exercises

Solve each equation. Round to the nearest tenth if necessary.

1. Sin $\theta = 0.8$

2. Tan $\theta = 4.5$

3. Cos $\theta = 0.5$

4. Cos $\theta = -0.95$

5. Sin $\theta = -0.1$

6. Tan $\theta = -1$

7. Cos $\theta = 0.52$

8. Cos $\theta = -0.2$

9. Sin $\theta = 0.35$

10. Tan $\theta = 8$

13-9 Skills Practice

Inverse Trigonometric Functions

Find each value. Write angle measures in degrees and radians.

1. $\text{Sin}^{-1} \dfrac{\sqrt{2}}{2}$

2. $\text{Cos}^{-1}\left(-\dfrac{\sqrt{3}}{2}\right)$

3. $\text{Tan}^{-1} \sqrt{3}$

4. $\text{Arctan}\left(-\dfrac{\sqrt{3}}{3}\right)$

5. $\text{Arccos}\left(-\dfrac{\sqrt{2}}{2}\right)$

6. $\text{Arcsin } 1$

Find each value. Round to the nearest hundredth of necessary.

7. $\sin\left(\text{Cos}^{-1} 1\right)$

8. $\sin\left(\text{Sin}^{-1} \dfrac{1}{2}\right)$

9. $\tan\left(\text{Arcsin} \dfrac{\sqrt{3}}{2}\right)$

10. $\cos\left(\text{Tan}^{-1} 3\right)$

11. $\sin\left[\text{Arctan}\left(-1\right)\right]$

12. $\sin\left[\text{Arccos}\left(-\dfrac{\sqrt{2}}{2}\right)\right]$

Solve each equation. Round to the nearest tenth if necessary.

13. $\cos \theta = 0.25$

14. $\sin \theta = -0.57$

15. $\tan \theta = 5$

16. $\cos \theta = 0.11$

17. $\sin \theta = 0.9$

18. $\tan \theta = -11.35$

19. $\sin \theta = 1$

20. $\tan \theta = -0.01$

21. $\cos \theta = -0.36$

22. $\tan \theta = -16.6$

Lesson 13-9

13-9 Practice

Inverse Trigonometric Functions

Find each value. Write angle measures in degrees and radians.

1. Arcsin 1

2. $\mathrm{Cos}^{-1}\left(\dfrac{-\sqrt{2}}{2}\right)$

3. $\mathrm{Tan}^{-1}\left(\dfrac{-\sqrt{3}}{3}\right)$

4. Arccos $\dfrac{\sqrt{2}}{2}$

5. Arctan $(-\sqrt{3})$

6. $\mathrm{Sin}^{-1}\left(-\dfrac{1}{2}\right)$

Find each value. Round to the nearest hundredth if necessary.

7. $\tan\left(\mathrm{Cos}^{-1}\dfrac{1}{2}\right)$

8. $\cos\left[\mathrm{Sin}^{-1}\left(-\dfrac{3}{5}\right)\right]$

9. $\cos\left[\mathrm{Arctan}\,(-1)\right]$

10. $\tan\left(\mathrm{Sin}^{-1}\dfrac{12}{13}\right)$

11. $\sin\left(\mathrm{Arctan}\,\dfrac{\sqrt{3}}{3}\right)$

12. $\cos\left(\mathrm{Arctan}\,\dfrac{3}{4}\right)$

Solve each equation. Round to the nearest tenth if necessary.

13. $\mathrm{Tan}\,\theta = 10$

14. $\mathrm{Sin}\,\theta = 0.7$

15. $\mathrm{Sin}\,\theta = -0.5$

16. $\mathrm{Cos}\,\theta = 0.05$

17. $\mathrm{Tan}\,\theta = 0.22$

18. $\mathrm{Sin}\,\theta = -0.03$

19. PULLEYS The equation $\cos\theta = 0.95$ describes the angle through which pulley A moves, and $\cos\theta = 0.17$ describes the angle through which pulley B moves. Which pulley moves through a greater angle?

20. FLYWHEELS The equation $\mathrm{Tan}\,\theta = 1$ describes the counterclockwise angle through which a flywheel rotates in 1 millisecond. Through how many degrees has the flywheel rotated after 25 milliseconds?

13-9 Word Problem Practice

Inverse Trigonometric Functions

1. DOORS The exit from a restaurant kitchen has a pair of swinging doors that meet in the middle of the doorway. Each door is three feet wide. A waiter needs to take a cart of plates into the dining area from the kitchen. The cart is two feet wide.

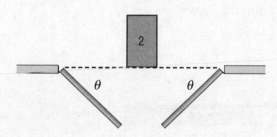

a. What is the minimum angle θ through which the doors must each be opened to prevent the cart from hitting either door?

b. If only one of the two doors could be opened, what is the minimum angle θ through which the door must be opened to prevent the cart from hitting the door?

c. If the pair of swinging doors were replaced by a single door the full width of the opening, what is the minimum angle θ through which the door must be opened to prevent the cart from hitting the door?

2. SURVEYING In ancient times, it was known that a triangle with side lengths of 3, 4, and 5 units was a right triangle. Surveyors used ropes with knots at each unit of length to make sure that an angle was a right angle. Such a rope was placed on the ground so that one leg of the triangle had three knots and the other had four. This guaranteed that the triangle formed was right triangle, meaning that the surveyor had formed a right angle.

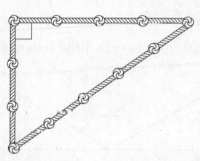

To the nearest degree, what are the angle measures in a triangle formed in this way?

3. TRAVEL Beth is riding her bike to her friend Marco's house. She can only ride on the streets, which run north-south or east-west.

a. Beth rides two miles east and four miles south to get to Marco's. If Beth could have traveled directly from her house to Marco's, in what direction would she have traveled?

b. Beth then rides three miles west and one mile north to get to the grocery store. If Beth could have traveled directly from Marco's house to the store, in what direction would she have traveled?

Lesson 13-9

13-9 Enrichment

Snell's Law

Snell's Law describes what happens to a ray of light that passes from air into water or some other substance. In the figure, the ray starts at the left and makes an angle of incidence θ with the surface.

Part of the ray is reflected, creating an angle of reflection θ. The rest of the ray is bent, or refracted, as it passes through the other medium. This creates angle θ'.

The angle of incidence equals the angle of reflection.

The angles of incidence and refraction are related by Snell's Law:

$\sin \theta = k \sin \theta'$

The constant k is called the index of refraction.

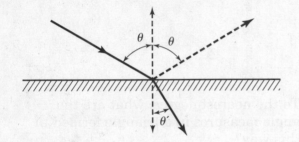

k	Substance
1.33	Water
1.36	Ethyl alcohol
1.54	Rock salt and Quartz
1.46–1.96	Glass
2.42	Diamond

Use Snell's Law to solve the following. Round angle measures to the nearest tenth of a degree.

1. If the angle of incidence at which a ray of light strikes the surface of a window is 45° and $k = 1.6$, what is the measure of the angle of refraction?

2. If the angle of incidence of a ray of light that strikes the surface of water is 50°, what is the angle of refraction?

3. If the angle of refraction of a ray of light striking a quartz crystal is 24°, what is the angle of incidence?

4. The angles of incidence and refraction for rays of light were measured five times for a certain substance. The measurements (one of which was in error) are shown in the table. Was the substance glass, quartz, or diamond?

θ	15°	30°	40°	60°	80°
θ'	9.7°	16.1°	21.2°	28.6°	33.2°

5. If the angle of incidence at which a ray of light strikes the surface of ethyl alcohol is 60°, what is the angle of refraction?

13 | Student Recording Sheet

Use this recording sheet with pages 886–887 of the Student Edition.

Multiple Choice

Read each question. Then fill in the correct answer.

1. Ⓐ Ⓑ Ⓒ Ⓓ   5. Ⓐ Ⓑ Ⓒ Ⓓ   9. Ⓐ Ⓑ Ⓒ Ⓓ

2. Ⓕ Ⓖ Ⓗ Ⓘ   6. Ⓕ Ⓖ Ⓗ Ⓘ   10. Ⓕ Ⓖ Ⓗ Ⓘ

3. Ⓐ Ⓑ Ⓒ Ⓓ   7. Ⓐ Ⓑ Ⓒ Ⓓ

4. Ⓕ Ⓖ Ⓗ Ⓘ   8. Ⓕ Ⓖ Ⓗ Ⓘ

Short Response/Gridded Response

Record your answer in the blank.

For gridded response questions, also enter your answer in the grid by writing each number or symbol in a box. Then fill in the corresponding circle for that number or symbol.

11. _____

12. _____ *(grid in)*

13. a. _____

     b. _____

     c. _____

14. _____ *(grid in)*

15. _____

16. _____ *(grid in)*

12.

14.

16.

Assessment

Extended Response

Record your answers for Question 17 on the back of this paper.

13 Rubric for Scoring Extended Response

General Scoring Guidelines

- If a student gives only a correct numerical answer to a problem but does not show how he or she arrived at the answer, the student will be awarded only 1 credit. All extended response questions require the student to show work.

- A fully correct answer for a multiple-part question requires correct responses for all parts of the question. For example, if a question has three parts, the correct response to one or two parts of the question that required work to be shown is *not* considered a fully correct response.

- Students who use trial and error to solve a problem must show their method. Merely showing that the answer checks or is correct is not considered a complete response for full credit.

Exercise 17 Rubric

Score	Specific Criteria
4	A correct solution that is supported by well-developed, accurate explanations.
3	A generally correct solution, but may contain minor flaws in reasoning or computation.
2	A partially correct interpretation and/or solution to the problem.
1	A correct solution with no supporting evidence or explanation.
0	An incorrect solution indicating no mathematical understanding of the concept or task, or no solution is given.

13 Chapter 13 Quiz 1

(Lessons 13-1 through 13-3)

SCORE _____

1. Find the values of the six trigonometric functions for angle θ.

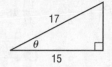

1. _____

2. **MULTIPLE CHOICE** If $\sin A = \dfrac{7}{10}$, find the value of $\cos A$.

   A $\dfrac{7\sqrt{149}}{149}$ **B** $\dfrac{\sqrt{51}}{10}$ **C** $\dfrac{10}{7}$ **D** $\dfrac{\sqrt{51}}{7}$

2. _____

Draw an angle with the given measure in standard position. Find an angle with a positive measure and an angle with a negative measure that are coterminal with each angle.

3. $-225°$

4. $\dfrac{\pi}{3}$

3. _____

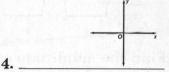

4. _____

5. Find the exact values of the six trigonometric functions of θ if the terminal side of θ in standard position contains the point $(-3, 1)$.

5. _____

----

13 Chapter 13 Quiz 2

(Lessons 13-4 and 13-5)

SCORE _____

1. **MULTIPLE CHOICE** Find the area of $\triangle ABC$ if $C = 15°$, $a = 12$ centimeters, and $b = 15$ centimeters.

   A 173.9 cm² **B** 86.9 cm² **C** 46.6 cm² **D** 23.3 cm²

1. _____

Determine whether each triangle should be solved by beginning with the Law of *Sines* or Law of *Cosines*. Then solve each triangle. Round to the nearest tenth.

2.

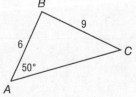

2. _____

3.

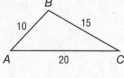

3. _____

4. $A = 36°$, $b = 6$, $c = 12$

4. _____

5. $a = 14$, $b = 8$, $c = 5$

5. _____

Assessment

13   Chapter 13 Quiz 3

(Lessons 13-6 and 13-7)

SCORE _____

1. MULTIPLE CHOICE $P\left(-\dfrac{\sqrt{3}}{2}, -\dfrac{1}{2}\right)$ is located on the unit circle. Find $\sin \theta$ and $\cos \theta$.

A $-\dfrac{\sqrt{3}}{2}, -\dfrac{1}{2}$ **C** $\dfrac{\sqrt{3}}{2}, \dfrac{1}{2}$

B $-\dfrac{1}{2}, -\dfrac{\sqrt{3}}{2}$ **D** $\dfrac{1}{2}, \dfrac{\sqrt{3}}{2}$

1. _____

Determine the period of each function.

2.

3.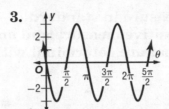

2. _____

3. _____

4. _____

Find the amplitude and period of each function.

4. $y = \dfrac{3}{4} \cos \dfrac{1}{2}\theta$ **5.** $y = 6 \csc 2\theta$

5. _____

- -

13   Chapter 13 Quiz 4

(Lessons 13-8 and 13-9)

SCORE _____

State the amplitude, period, vertical shift, and phase shift for each function.

1. $y = -1 + 2 \cos \dfrac{4}{3}\left(\theta + \dfrac{3\pi}{2}\right)$

1. _____

2. $y = 3 \tan \dfrac{5}{6}(\theta - 45°) + 2$

2. _____

Find each value. Round to the nearest hundredth if necessary.

3. $\text{Cos}^{-1} 1$

3. _____

4. $\cos\left[\text{Sin}^{-1}\left(-\dfrac{3}{5}\right)\right]$

4. _____

5. MULTIPLE CHOICE Evaluate $\cot\left(\text{Arccos} \dfrac{1}{6}\right)$.

A 57.29   **B** 5.92   **C** 0.17   **D** 0.09

5. _____

13 Chapter 13 Mid-Chapter Test

SCORE _____

(Lessons 13-1 through 13-5)

Part I Write the letter for the correct answer in the blank at the right of each question.

1. If $\sin A = \dfrac{3}{5}$, find $\cos A$.

    A $\dfrac{3}{4}$ **B** $\dfrac{4}{5}$ **C** $\dfrac{5}{3}$ **D** $\dfrac{4}{3}$ 1. _____

2. Rewrite 75° in radian measure.

    F $\dfrac{5\pi}{6}$ **G** $\dfrac{5\pi}{12}$ **H** $\dfrac{5}{12}$ **J** $\dfrac{\pi}{5}$ 2. _____

3. Rewrite $\dfrac{3\pi}{4}$ radians in degree measure.

    A 135°   **B** 540°   **C** 270°   **D** 240°   3. _____

4. Which angle is coterminal with 590°?

    F 130°   **G** 50°   **H** 230°   **J** −140°   4. _____

5. Which trigonometric function has a value of 0?

    A $\tan \dfrac{\pi}{2}$ **B** $\sin 180°$ **C** $\cos \pi$ **D** $\cot 0°$ 5. _____

6. Find the exact value of $\sin 240°$.

    F $-\sqrt{3}$ **G** $-\dfrac{\sqrt{3}}{2}$ **H** $-\dfrac{1}{2}$ **J** $\dfrac{1}{\sqrt{3}}$ 6. _____

Part II

7. Find the values of the six trigonometric functions for angle θ.

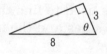

    7. _____

8. Solve $\triangle ABC$ if $A = 40°$, $C = 90°$, and $b = 10$. Round measures of sides to the nearest tenth and measures of angles to the nearest degree.

    8. _____

9. Find the exact values of the six trigonometric functions of θ if the terminal side of θ in standard position contains the point $(-3, 6)$.

    9. _____

10. Find the area of $\triangle ABC$ if $A = 98°$, $b = 45$ feet, and $c = 61$ feet. Round to the nearest tenth.

    10. _____

Determine whether each triangle has *no* solution, *one* solution, or *two* solutions. Then solve each triangle. Round to the nearest tenth.

11. $A = 52°$, $a = 7$, $b = 3$ 11. _____

12. $A = 137°$, $a = 10$, $b = 15$ 12. _____

Assessment

13 Chapter 13 Vocabulary Test

SCORE _____

angle of depression	cosine	Law of Sines	sine
angle of elevation	cotangent	period	standard position
amplitude	cycle	periodic function	tangent
circular function	frequency	radian	trigonometry
cosecant	Law of Cosines	secant	unit circle

Choose the letter of the term that best matches each phrase.

_____ 1. the number of cycles in a given unit of time

_____ 2. the ratio of the length of the side adjacent to an acute angle of a right triangle to the length of the hypotenuse

_____ 3. the formula that is used to solve a triangle when two angles and one side are known

_____ 4. a function where the *y*-values repeat at regular intervals

_____ 5. the angle between a line parallel to the ground and the line of sight to an object

_____ 6. one complete pattern of a periodic function

_____ 7. the formula that is used to find the third side of a triangle when two sides and the included angle are known

_____ 8. the ratio of the length of the side opposite an acute angle of a right triangle to the length of the adjacent side

_____ 9. the reciprocal of the cosine function

_____ 10. the reciprocal of the sine function

a. Law of Cosines

b. tangent

c. periodic function

d. secant

e. frequency

f. cosecant

g. Law of Sines

h. cosine

i. cycle

j. angle of elevation

Define each term.

11. standard position

12. unit circle

13   Chapter 13 Test, Form 1

SCORE _____

Write the letter for the correct answer in the blank at the right of each question.

1. Find the value of $\tan \theta$.

  A $\frac{4}{3}$ **C** $\frac{3}{4}$

  B $\frac{4}{5}$ **D** $\frac{5}{3}$

1. _____

2. Which equation can be used to find x?

  F $\cos 60° = \frac{4}{x}$ **H** $\tan 60° = \frac{x}{4}$

  G $\sin 60° = \frac{4}{x}$ **J** $\cot 60° = \frac{4}{x}$

2. _____

3. Find P to the nearest degree.

  A $21°$ **C** $23°$

  B $67°$ **D** $69°$

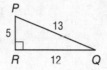

3. _____

4. Rewrite $90°$ in radian measure.

  F $\frac{\pi}{2}$ **G** $\frac{\pi}{90}$ **H** $\frac{\pi}{4}$ **J** $\frac{2}{\pi}$

4. _____

5. Rewrite $\frac{\pi}{6}$ radians in degree measure.

  A $30\pi°$ **B** $30°$ **C** $120°$ **D** $60°$

5. _____

6. Which angle is coterminal with a $90°$ angle in standard position?

  F $540°$ **G** $450°$ **H** $-90°$ **J** $270°$

6. _____

7. Find the exact value of $\cos \theta$ if the terminal side of θ in standard position contains the point $(8, 15)$.

  A $\frac{17}{8}$ **B** $\frac{8}{17}$ **C** $\frac{8}{15}$ **D** $\frac{15}{17}$

7. _____

8. What is the reference angle for $150°$?

  F $150°$ **G** $60°$ **H** $-210°$ **J** $30°$

8. _____

9. Find the exact value of $\sin 150°$.

  A $-\frac{\sqrt{3}}{2}$ **B** $\frac{\sqrt{3}}{2}$ **C** $\frac{1}{2}$ **D** $-\frac{1}{2}$

9. _____

10. Which formula can be used to find the area of $\triangle ABC$?

  F area $= \frac{1}{2}ac \sin C$ **H** area $= \frac{1}{2}ab \sin A$

  G area $= \frac{1}{2}bc \sin A$ **J** area $= \frac{1}{2}bc \sin B$

10. _____

11. In $\triangle ABC$, $A = 42°$, $C = 56°$, and $a = 12$. Find c.

   A 9.7   **B** 21.6   **C** 16.0   **D** 14.9   **11.** _____

12. Determine the number of solutions for $\triangle ABC$ if $A = 139°$, $a = 12$, and $b = 19$.

   F no solution   **G** 1 solution   **H** 2 solutions   **J** 3 solutions   **12.** _____

13. In $\triangle ABC$, find a if $b = 2$, $c = 6$, and $A = 35°$.

   A 20.3   **B** 7.7   **C** 5.5   **D** 4.5   **13.** _____

14. Which triangle should be solved by beginning with the Law of Cosines?

   F $A = 20°$, $C = 50°$, $b = 3$ **H** $a = 13$, $b = 24$, $c = 24$

   G $A = 30°$, $a = 5$, $b = 7$ **J** $B = 45°$, $C = 25°$, $c = 10$ **14.** _____

15. $P\left(-\frac{4}{5}, -\frac{3}{5}\right)$ is located on the unit circle. Find $\cos\theta$.

   A $\frac{4}{5}$ **B** $-\frac{4}{5}$ **C** $-\frac{3}{5}$ **D** $\frac{3}{4}$ **15.** _____

16. Determine the period of the function.

   F 2   **H** 8

   G 3   **J** 4   **16.** _____

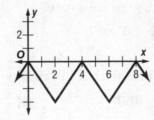

17. Find the period of $y = 2\tan\frac{2}{3}\theta$.

   A 540°   **B** 270°   **C** 240°   **D** 120°   **17.** _____

18. Find the phase shift of $y = 3 + 2\cos(\theta + 90°)$.

   F 2   **G** 3   **H** 90°   **J** −90°   **18.** _____

19. Solve $y = \text{Sin}^{-1}\frac{\sqrt{3}}{2}$.

   A 30°   **B** 60°   **C** 45°   **D** 90°   **19.** _____

20. Find the value of $\text{Sin}^{-1}(-1)$.

   F 30°   **G** −45°   **H** 180°   **J** −90°   **20.** _____

Bonus Find the perimeter of $\triangle ABC$ to the nearest tenth if $A = 25°$, $C = 90°$, and $c = 10$ meters.   **B:** _____

13   Chapter 13 Test, Form 2A

SCORE _____

Write the letter for the correct answer in the blank at the right of each question.

1. Find the value of csc A.

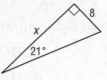

  A $\frac{8}{17}$ **C** $\frac{17}{15}$

  B $\frac{17}{8}$ **D** $\frac{15}{17}$

                                                        1. _____

2. Which equation can be used to find x?

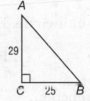

  F $\sin 21° = \frac{8}{x}$ **H** $\tan 21° = \frac{x}{8}$

  G $\tan 21° = \frac{8}{x}$ **J** $\sin 21° = \frac{x}{8}$

                                                        2. _____

3. Find A to the nearest degree.

  A 49°   **C** 37°

  B 41°   **D** 53°

                                                           3. _____

4. Rewrite $\frac{2\pi}{9}$ radians in degree measure.

  F 20°   **G** 80°   **H** 40°   **J** $\frac{40°}{\pi}$ **4.** _____

5. Which angle is coterminal with an angle in standard position measuring $-\frac{5\pi}{9}$?

  A $\frac{13\pi}{9}$ **B** $\frac{5\pi}{9}$ **C** $\frac{23\pi}{9}$ **D** $\frac{10\pi}{9}$ **5.** _____

6. Find the exact value of $\sin \theta$ if the terminal side of θ in standard position contains the point $(-4, -3)$.

  F $-\frac{4}{5}$ **G** $-\frac{3}{5}$ **H** $\frac{3}{5}$ **J** $\frac{4}{5}$ **6.** _____

7. Find the exact value of cot 450°.

  A 0   **B** undefined   **C** 1   **D** −1   **7.** _____

8. Find the exact value of $\cos\left(-\frac{\pi}{4}\right)$.

  F $\frac{\sqrt{2}}{2}$ **G** $-\frac{\sqrt{2}}{2}$ **H** $\frac{\sqrt{3}}{2}$ **J** $-\frac{\sqrt{3}}{2}$ **8.** _____

9. In $\triangle ABC$, $A = 40°$, $B = 60°$, and $a = 5$. Find b.

  A 6.4   **B** 7.5   **C** 6.7   **D** 3.7   **9.** _____

10. Find the area of $\triangle ABC$ if $A = 72°$, $b = 9$ feet, and $c = 10$ feet.

  F 85.6 ft²   **G** 42.8 ft²   **H** 45.0 ft²   **J** 13.9 ft²   **10.** _____

Assessment

11. Which triangle has two solutions?

   A $A = 130°, a = 19, b = 11$ **C** $A = 45°, a = 4\sqrt{2}, b = 8$

   B $A = 32°, a = 16, b = 21$ **D** $A = 90°, a = 25, c = 15$ **11.** _____

12. In $\triangle ABC$, $C = 60°$, $a = 12$, and $b = 5$. Find c.

   F 109.0   **G** 10.4   **H** 11.8   **J** 15.1   **12.** _____

13. Which triangle should be solved by beginning with the Law of Cosines?

   A $A = 115°, a = 19, b = 13$ **C** $A = 62°, B = 15°, b = 10$

   B $B = 48°, a = 22, b = 5$ **D** $A = 50°, b = 20, c = 18$ **13.** _____

14. $P\left(-\dfrac{9}{41}, \dfrac{40}{41}\right)$ is located on the unit circle. Find $\sin \theta$.

   F $\dfrac{40}{41}$ **G** $-\dfrac{9}{41}$ **H** $-\dfrac{9}{40}$ **J** $-\dfrac{40}{9}$ **14.** _____

15. Determine the period of the function.

   A 2   **C** 3

   B 6   **D** 1   **15.** _____

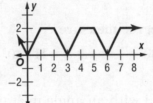

16. Find the period of $y = 4 \cos \dfrac{5}{2}\theta$.

   F 900°   **G** 450°   **H** 144°   **J** 72°   **16.** _____

17. Find the phase shift of $y = -3 + \tan \dfrac{1}{2}\left(\theta + \dfrac{\pi}{2}\right)$.

   A -3 **B** $\dfrac{1}{2}$ **C** $-\dfrac{\pi}{2}$ **D** $\dfrac{\pi}{2}$ **17.** _____

18. Write the equation $\sin y = x$ in the form of an inverse function.

   F $y = \sin^{-1} x$ **G** $x = \sin^{-1} y$ **H** $x = \sin y$ **J** $y = \sin x$ **18.** _____

19. Solve $y = \text{Arcsin } \dfrac{1}{2}$.

   A $-\dfrac{5\pi}{6}$ **B** $\dfrac{5\pi}{6}$ **C** $-\dfrac{\pi}{6}$ **D** $\dfrac{\pi}{6}$ **19.** _____

20. Find the value of $\tan\left(\text{Tan}^{-1} \dfrac{1}{2}\right)$.

   F -1 **G** 1   **H** $\dfrac{1}{2}$ **J** $-\dfrac{1}{2}$ **20.** _____

Bonus From one point on the ground, the angle of elevation
to the top of a building is 35°, while 100 feet closer, the
angle of elevation is 45°. Find the height of the building
to the nearest foot.   **B:** _____

13 Chapter 13 Test, Form 2B

SCORE _____

Copyright © Glencoe/McGraw-Hill, a division of The McGraw-Hill Companies, Inc.

Write the letter for the correct answer in the blank at the right of each question.

1. Find the value of sec A.

   A $\dfrac{17}{8}$ **C** $\dfrac{8}{17}$

   B $\dfrac{15}{17}$ **D** $\dfrac{17}{15}$

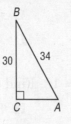

1. _____

2. Which equation can be used to find x?

   F $\sin 32° = \dfrac{x}{7}$ **H** $\cot 32° = \dfrac{7}{x}$

   G $\tan 32° = \dfrac{x}{7}$ **J** $\cos 32° = \dfrac{x}{7}$

2. _____

3. Find A to the nearest degree.

   A 55°   **C** 30°

   B 35°   **D** 60°

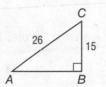

3. _____

4. Rewrite $\dfrac{5\pi}{4}$ radians in degree measure.

   F 450°   **G** 225°   **H** 225π°   **J** 112.5°

4. _____

5. Which angle is coterminal with a −400° angle in standard position?

   A 40°   **B** 80°   **C** 320°   **D** 400°

5. _____

6. Find the exact value of cos θ if the terminal side of θ in standard position contains the point (6, −8).

   F $-\dfrac{4}{5}$ **G** $\dfrac{3}{5}$ **H** $\dfrac{4}{5}$ **J** $-\dfrac{3}{5}$

6. _____

7. Find the exact value of cot (−315°).

   A 1   **B** $\sqrt{2}$ **C** $\dfrac{\sqrt{2}}{2}$ **D** 2

7. _____

8. Find the exact value of $\sin\left(-\dfrac{\pi}{6}\right)$.

   F $-\dfrac{1}{2}$ **G** $-\dfrac{\sqrt{3}}{2}$ **H** $-\dfrac{\sqrt{2}}{2}$ **J** $\dfrac{\sqrt{2}}{2}$

8. _____

9. In △ABC, $C = 30°$, $c = 22$, and $b = 42$. Find B.

   A 73°   **B** 117°   **C** 77°   **D** 15°

9. _____

10. Find the area of △ABC if $A = 55°$, $b = 8$ meters and $c = 14$ meters.

   F 91.7 m²   **G** 32.1 m²   **H** 45.9 m²   **J** 56.0 m²

10. _____

11. Which triangle has no solution?

   A $A = 45°, a = 3, b = 4$ **C** $A = 135°, a = 15, b = 9$

   B $A = 15°, a = 3, b = 19$ **D** $A = 69°, a = 12, b = 6$ **11.** _____

12. In $\triangle ABC$, $A = 15°$, $b = 19$, and $c = 12$. Find a.

   F 64.5   **G** 16.9   **H** 30.7   **J** 8.0   **12.** _____

13. Which triangle should be solved by beginning with the Law of Sines?

   A $A = 125°, B = 16°, a = 10$ **C** $A = 85°, b = 31, c = 24$

   B $B = 72°, a = 5, c = 17$ **D** $a = 13, b = 9, c = 15$ **13.** _____

14. $P\left(-\dfrac{40}{41}, -\dfrac{9}{41}\right)$ is located on the unit circle. Find $\cos\theta$.

   F $-\dfrac{9}{41}$ **G** $-\dfrac{40}{41}$ **H** $\dfrac{40}{9}$ **J** $-\dfrac{9}{40}$ **14.** _____

15. Determine the period of the function.

   A 60   **C** 48

   B 2   **D** 24   **15.** _____

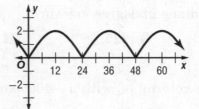

16. Find the period of $y = 2\sin\dfrac{2}{5}\theta$.

   F 900°   **G** 450°   **H** 144°   **J** 72°   **16.** _____

17. Find the vertical shift of $y = -3 + \tan\dfrac{1}{2}\left(\theta + \dfrac{\pi}{2}\right)$.

   A -3 **B** $\dfrac{1}{2}$ **C** $-\dfrac{\pi}{2}$ **D** $\dfrac{\pi}{2}$ **17.** _____

18. Write the equation $\tan b = c$ in the form of an inverse function.

   F $b = \tan c$ **G** $c = \text{Tan}^{-1} b$ **H** $b = \text{Tan}^{-1} c$ **J** $\tan = \dfrac{b}{c}$ **18.** _____

19. Solve $y = \text{Cos}^{-1}\dfrac{\sqrt{2}}{2}$.

   A $-135°$ **B** $-45°$ **C** $45°$ **D** $135°$ **19.** _____

20. Find the value of $\tan\left(\text{Arccos}\dfrac{1}{2}\right)$.

   F 1.36   **G** 0.58   **H** 1.73   **J** 0.02   **20.** _____

Bonus From one point on the ground, the angle of elevation
       to the top of a building is 34°, while 100 feet closer, the
       angle of elevation is 48°. Find the height of the building
       to the nearest foot.   **B:** _____

13 Chapter 13 Test, Form 2C

SCORE _____

Assessment

1. Find the values of the six trigonometric functions for angle θ.

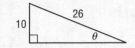

1. _____

2. Solve $\triangle ABC$ if $a = 3$, $c = 7$, and $C = 90°$. Round measures of sides to the nearest tenth and measures of angles to the nearest degree.

2. _____

3. Write an equation involving sin, cos, or tan that can be used to find x. Then solve the equation, rounding to the nearest degree.

3. _____

4. Rewrite $-75°$ in radian measure.

4. _____

5. Rewrite $\dfrac{5\pi}{3}$ radians in degree measure.

5. _____

6. Find one angle with positive measure and one angle with negative measure coterminal with an angle in standard position measuring $\dfrac{5\pi}{4}$.

6. _____

7. Find the exact values of the six trigonometric functions of θ if the terminal side of θ in standard position contains the point $(-4, -6)$.

7. _____

8. Sketch the angle with measure $\dfrac{5\pi}{3}$ radians. Then find its reference angle.

8.

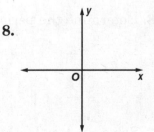

For Questions 9 and 10, find the exact value of each trigonometric function.

9. $\sin\left(-\dfrac{\pi}{3}\right)$

9. _____

10. $\cos 810°$

10. _____

11. Find the area of $\triangle ABC$ if $C = 74°$, $a = 21$ miles, and $b = 63$ miles. Round to the nearest tenth.

11. _____

**Determine whether each triangle has *no* solution, *one*
solution, or *two* solutions. Then solve each triangle.
Round to the nearest tenth.**

12. $A = 58°, a = 17, b = 12$ 13. $A = 110°, a = 6, b = 15$

12. _____

13. _____

**For Questions 14 and 15, determine whether each
triangle should be solved by beginning with the Law of
Sines or Law of *Cosines*. Then solve each triangle. Round
to the nearest tenth if necessary.**

14. $A = 70°, B = 80°, a = 9$ 15. $C = 114.6°, a = 5, b = 7$

14. _____

15. _____

16. Given an angle θ in standard position, if $P\left(-\frac{1}{2}, -\frac{\sqrt{3}}{2}\right)$ lies
   on the terminal side and on the unit circle, find $\sin \theta$ and
   $\cos \theta$.

16. _____

17. Find the amplitude, period, phase shift, and vertical shift
   of $y = 3 \csc \frac{3}{4}\left(\theta - \frac{\pi}{4}\right) - 1$.

17. _____

18. Determine the period of the function.

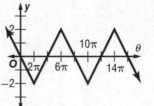

18. _____

19. Solve $x = \tan^{-1}(-1)$.

19. _____

20. Find the value of $\sin\left(\text{Arctan} \frac{\sqrt{3}}{3}\right)$. Round to the
   nearest hundredth.

20. _____

Bonus A tree is observed on the opposite bank of a river. At that
   point, the river is known to be 140 feet wide. The angle
   of elevation from a point 5 feet off the ground to the top
   of the tree is 20°. Find the height of the tree to the
   nearest foot.

B: _____

13 **Chapter 13 Test, Form 2D**

1. Find the values of the six trigonometric functions for angle θ.

1. _____

2. Solve $\triangle ABC$ if $c = 8$, $a = 5$, and $C = 90°$. Round measures of sides to the nearest tenth and measures of angles to the nearest degree.

2. _____

3. Write an equation involving sin, cos, or tan that can be used to find x. Then solve the equation, rounding to the nearest degree.

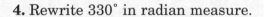

3. _____

4. Rewrite $330°$ in radian measure.

4. _____

5. Rewrite $-\dfrac{7\pi}{4}$ radians in degree measure.

5. _____

6. Find one angle with positive measure and one angle with negative measure coterminal with an angle in standard position measuring $-120°$.

6. _____

7. Find the exact values of the six trigonometric functions of θ if the terminal side of θ in standard position contains the point $(12, -8)$.

7. _____

8. Sketch the angle with measure $-\dfrac{7\pi}{4}$ radians. Then find its reference angle.

8. _____

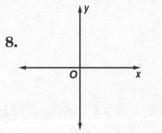

For Questions 9 and 10, find the exact value of each trigonometric function.

_____

9. $\cos \dfrac{2\pi}{3}$

9. _____

10. $\sin -630°$

10. _____

11. Find the area of $\triangle ABC$ if $C = 62°$, $a = 12$ yards, and $b = 9$ yards. Round to the nearest tenth.

11. _____

13   Chapter 13 Test, Form 2D   *(continued)*

Determine whether each triangle has *no* solution, *one* solution, or *two* solutions. Then solve each triangle. Round to the nearest tenth.

12. $A = 29°$, $a = 5$, $b = 14$ **13.** $A = 60°$, $a = 9$, $b = 6$ 12. _____

13. _____

For Questions 14 and 15, determine whether each triangle should be solved by beginning with the Law of *Sines* or Law of *Cosines*. Then solve each triangle. Round to the nearest tenth.

14. $A = 19°$, $a = 10$, $b = 8$ **15.** $C = 45°$, $a = 4$, $b = 9$ 14. _____

15. _____

16. Given an angle θ in standard position, if $P\left(\dfrac{\sqrt{3}}{2}, -\dfrac{1}{2}\right)$ lies on the terminal side and on the unit circle, find $\sin \theta$ and $\cos \theta$.   16. _____

17. Find the amplitude, period, phase shift, and vertical shift of $y = 2\cos \dfrac{4}{3}(\theta + 90°) - 2$.   17. _____

18. Determine the period of the function.   18. _____

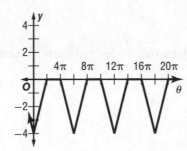

19. Solve $x = \text{Arcsin}\left(\dfrac{1}{2}\right)$.   19. _____

20. Find the value of $\tan\left(\text{Tan}^{-1} \dfrac{3}{8}\right)$. Round to the nearest hundredth.   20. _____

Bonus A tree is observed on the opposite bank of a river. At that point, the river is known to be 120 feet wide. The angle of elevation from a point 4 feet off the ground to the top of the tree is 25°. Find the height of the tree to the nearest foot.   B: _____

13 **Chapter 13 Test, Form 3**

SCORE _____

Copyright © Glencoe/McGraw-Hill, a division of The McGraw-Hill Companies, Inc.

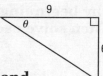

1. Find the values of the six trigonometric functions for angle θ.

1. _____

Solve △ABC using the diagram at the right and the given measurements. Round measures of sides to the nearest tenth and measures of angles to the nearest degree.

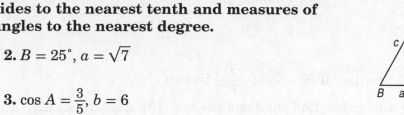

2. $B = 25°$, $a = \sqrt{7}$

2. _____

3. $\cos A = \dfrac{3}{5}$, $b = 6$

3. _____

For Questions 4 and 5, rewrite each degree measure in radians and each radian measure in degrees.

4. $-315°$

4. _____

5. -5

5. _____

6. Find one angle with positive measure and one angle with negative measure coterminal with $723°$.

6. _____

7. Find the exact values of the six trigonometric functions of θ if the terminal side of θ in standard position contains the point $(-\sqrt{3}, 1)$.

7. _____

For Questions 8 and 9, find the exact value of each trigonometric function.

8. $\cos(-300°)$

8. _____

9. $\cot \dfrac{9\pi}{4}$

9. _____

10. In △ABC, $a = 12$ meters, $b = 9$ meters, and $c = 6$ meters. Find the area of △ABC. Round to the nearest tenth.

10. _____

Determine whether each triangle has *no* solution, *one* solution, or *two* solutions. Then solve each triangle. Round to the nearest tenth.

11. $A = 42°$, $a = 9$, $b = 12$

11. _____

12. $A = 59°$, $a = 10$, $b = 7$

12. _____

13   Chapter 13 Test, Form 3   *(continued)*

For Questions 13 and 14, determine whether each triangle should be solved by beginning with the Law of *Sines* or Law of *Cosines*. Then solve each triangle. Round to the nearest tenth.

13. $C = 40.1°, a = 3, b = 8.2$

13. _____

14. $C = 132°, a = 15, c = 26$

14. _____

15. Given an angle θ in standard position, if $P\left(-\dfrac{2\sqrt{7}}{7}, \dfrac{\sqrt{21}}{7}\right)$ lies on

the terminal side and on the unit circle, find $\sin\theta$ and $\cos\theta$.   15. _____

For Questions 16 and 17, find the exact value of each function.

16. $\sin\dfrac{19\pi}{6}$

16. _____

17. $3(\sin 120°)(\cos 120°)$

17. _____

18. Determine the period of the function.

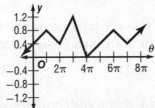

18. _____

19. Find the amplitude, period, phase shift, and vertical shift

of $y = 8\cot\dfrac{12}{7}(\theta + 45°) + 5$.   19. _____

20. Find the value of $\cos\left(2\,\text{Sin}^{-1}\dfrac{4}{5}\right)$. Round to the nearest

hundredth.   20. _____

Bonus   Given $\triangle ABC$ with $A = 27°$. Point X lies on $\overline{AC}$ such that $BX = 8$ meters and $\angle BXC$ has measure $142°$. The area of $\triangle BXC$ is 21.9 square meters. Find the perimeter of $\triangle ABC$ to the nearest tenth.   **B:** _____

13 Chapter 13 Extended-Response Test

SCORE _____

Demonstrate your knowledge by giving a clear, concise solution
to each problem. Be sure to include all relevant drawings and
justify your answers. You may show your solution in more than
one way or investigate beyond the requirements of the problem.

1. Stakes driven at points A and B in the diagram
   indicate where a new bridge will be built over
   the body of water shown. Monica, a surveyor,
   must determine the length c of the new bridge.
   She drives a third stake at point C, then uses a
   transit to determine the measures of angles A,
   B, and C.

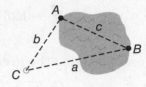

   a. Explain why Monica does not yet have enough information to find c.

   b. What additional information can she determine to help her find c?

   c. Select reasonable measures for angles A, B, and C, and for the information you
   suggested in part **b**. Then determine the length of the bridge to the nearest whole
   unit. Explain your method.

2. For $\triangle XYZ$ with $X = 24°$, $Z = 90°$, $y = 13.7$, and $z = 15$, show three distinctly different
   ways to find the length x of the third side of the triangle. Round to the nearest tenth.

3. Select any point P in Quadrant III. Explain how to find the measure of θ if the terminal
   side of θ in standard position contains your point P. Round to the nearest degree.

4. The area of a sector with radius r and central

   angle θ is given by $A = \frac{1}{2}r^2\theta$, where θ is

   measured in radians. Select any point Q in
   Quadrant I. Explain how to find the area of the
   sector bounded by θ, whose terminal side contains
   your point Q, and the arc intercepted by θ (the area
   shaded in the figure). Round to the nearest tenth.

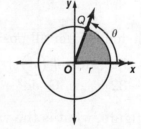

5. a. Explain how to find the area of $\triangle ABC$ with $C = 45°$, $b = 18$ inches, and

   $c = 9\sqrt{2}$ inches using the formula area $= \frac{1}{2}bc \sin A$ or $\frac{1}{2}ac \sin B$ or $\frac{1}{2}ab \sin C$.
   Determine the exact area.

   b. Is it possible to find this area using the formula area = (base)(height)? Explain your
   reasoning.

   c. Explain the relationship, if any, between the two formulas.

Assessment

13 Standardized Test Practice

(Chapters 1–13)

SCORE _____

Part 1: Multiple Choice

Instructions: Fill in the appropriate circle for the best answer.

1. Which real number is irrational?

   A $\frac{27}{5}$ **B** -0.257 **C** $0.\overline{257}$ **D** $0.2573...$ 1. Ⓐ Ⓑ Ⓒ Ⓓ

2. Which expression is the greatest in value?

   F $27 \div \frac{1}{3}$ **G** $27 + \frac{1}{3}$ **H** $27 \cdot \frac{1}{3}$ **J** $27^{\frac{1}{3}}$ 2. Ⓕ Ⓖ Ⓗ Ⓙ

3. Point B lies between points A and C such that the lengths AB and BC are in the ratio 2:5. If $\overline{AB}$ is 30 units in length, what is the length of $\overline{AC}$?

   A 75 **B** 105 **C** 150 **D** 42   3. Ⓐ Ⓑ Ⓒ Ⓓ

4. What is the sum of the whole numbers that are factors of 36?

   F 97 **G** 91 **H** 85 **J** 54   4. Ⓕ Ⓖ Ⓗ Ⓙ

5. What is the area of the shaded region in the figure if the perimeter of square $QRST$ is 48 units?

   A $72 - 18\pi$ **C** $72 - 6\pi$

   B $144 - 36\pi$ **D** $72 - 72\pi$

   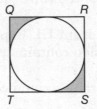

   5. Ⓐ Ⓑ Ⓒ Ⓓ

6. If ⓧ is defined, for all positive integers x, to be ⓧ $= 4\sqrt[3]{x}$, what is the value of ⓐ⁶ + ④³?

   F $4a^3 + 32$ **G** $4a^2 + 4$ **H** $4a^2 + 16$ **J** $4a^3 + 16$ 6. Ⓕ Ⓖ Ⓗ Ⓙ

7. In the figure, what is the value of x?

   A 3 **C** 45

   B 61 **D** 31

   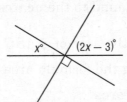

   7. Ⓐ Ⓑ Ⓒ Ⓓ

8. What is the sum of the squares of the roots of the equation $x^2 + 2x = 80$?

   F -36 **G** 164 **H** 4 **J** 416   8. Ⓕ Ⓖ Ⓗ Ⓙ

9. What is the length of the diameter of the base of a cylinder if its volume is 768π cubic inches and its height is 12 inches?

   A 16 in. **B** 8 in. **C** 8π in. **D** 64 in.   9. Ⓐ Ⓑ Ⓒ Ⓓ

10. Five people are to be seated in a row on the stage during a graduation ceremony. In how many different ways can the people be arranged?

    F 5 **G** 15 **H** 24 **J** 120   10. Ⓕ Ⓖ Ⓗ Ⓙ

13 Standardized Test Practice (continued)
(Chapters 1–13)

11. Find the distance between $(2, 5)$ and $(-4, 1)$.

    A $\sqrt{34}$ **B** $2\sqrt{13}$ **C** $4\sqrt{2}$ **D** $6\sqrt{2}$ 11. Ⓐ Ⓑ Ⓒ Ⓓ

12. Write $9x^2 = 4y^2 - 16y + 52$ in standard form.

    F $\dfrac{x^2}{4} - \dfrac{(y-2)^2}{9} = 1$ **H** $\dfrac{x^2}{4} - \dfrac{(y+2)^2}{9} = 1$

    G $\dfrac{x^2}{4} + \dfrac{(y-2)^2}{9} = 1$ **J** $\dfrac{x^2}{4} + \dfrac{(y+2)^2}{9} = 1$ 12. Ⓕ Ⓖ Ⓗ Ⓙ

13. Which system of inequalities is graphed?

    A $x^2 + y^2 \le 16$ **C** $x^2 + y^2 \le 16$
        $x^2 + 16y^2 \ge 16$ $16x^2 + y^2 \ge 16$

    B $x^2 + y^2 \ge 16$ **D** $x^2 + y^2 \le 16$
        $16x^2 + y^2 \le 16$ $\dfrac{x^2}{16} + y^2 \ge 1$ 13. Ⓐ Ⓑ Ⓒ Ⓓ

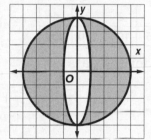

14. Simplify $\dfrac{5t^2 - 45}{4(t+3)^2} \cdot \dfrac{2t+6}{5t-15}$.

    F $\dfrac{(t-3)^0}{(t+3)^2}$ **G** $\dfrac{t^2-9}{(t+3)(t-3)}$ **H** $\dfrac{1}{2}$ **J** $\dfrac{2}{5}$ 14. Ⓕ Ⓖ Ⓗ Ⓙ

Part 2: Gridded Response

Instructions: Enter your answer by writing each digit of the answer in a column box and then shading in the appropriate circle that corresponds to that entry.

15. The circle graph shows the results of a survey of elementary school students who were asked to select their favorite color. What percent of the students selected orange?

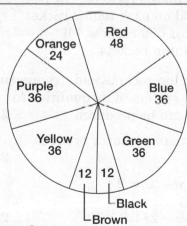

16. What is the 14th term of the sequence 1, 4, 9, 16, 25, …?

17. If one decasecond is equivalent to 10 seconds, how many decaseconds are equivalent to 2 hours?

18. By how much does twice the sum of 50 and 20 exceed the quotient of 80 and 20?

15.   16.

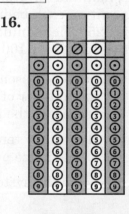

17.   18.

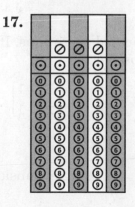

13 Standardized Test Practice (continued)

(Chapters 1–13)

Part 2: Short Response

Instructions: Write your answers in the space provided.

19. Solve $5 \mid 2a + 5 \mid - 4 \leq 6$ and graph the solution set.

19. _____

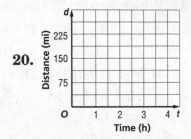

For Questions 20 and 21, use the data in the table below that shows the relationship between the distance traveled and the elapsed time for a trip.

Time t (h)	0	1	2	3	4
Distance d (mi)	0	55	100	150	260

20. Draw a scatter plot for the data.

20.

21. Use two ordered pairs to write a prediction equation. Then use your prediction equation to predict the distance traveled in an elapsed time of 6 hours.

21. _____

22. Classify the system $x + 9y = 10$ and $2x - y = 1$ as *consistent and independent*, *consistent and dependent*, or *inconsistent*.

22. _____

For Questions 23 and 24, use the following information.
A manufacturer produces badminton and tennis rackets. The profit on each badminton racket is $10 and on each tennis racket is $25. The manufacturer can make at most 600 rackets. Of these, at least 100 rackets must be badminton rackets.

23. Let b represent the number of badminton rackets and t represent the number of tennis rackets. Write a system of inequalities to represent the number of rackets that can be produced.

23. _____

24. How many tennis rackets should the manufacturer produce to maximize profit?

24. _____

25. Solve the system of equations.
$$2x + y - 3z = 9$$
$$x - 2y + z = -8$$
$$x + 3y - 2z = 11$$

25. _____

26. Perform the indicated operations. If the matrix does not exist, write *impossible*.

$$\begin{bmatrix} 2 & -1 & 3 \\ 3 & 0 & -4 \end{bmatrix} \cdot \begin{bmatrix} -4 & 2 \\ 0 & -3 \\ -5 & 1 \end{bmatrix} - 4 \begin{bmatrix} -5 & 1 \\ 2 & -1 \end{bmatrix}$$

26. _____

27. Evaluate $\begin{vmatrix} 3 & 4 & 0 \\ 2 & 5 & -1 \\ 0 & 3 & -7 \end{vmatrix}$ using expansion by minors.

27. _____

Lesson 13-1

NAME _____ DATE _____ PERIOD _____

13-1 Study Guide and Intervention

Trigonometric Functions in Right Triangles

Trigonometric Functions for Acute Angles Trigonometry is the study of relationships among the angles and sides of a right triangle. A trigonometric function has a rule given by a **trigonometric ratio**, which is a ratio that compares the side lengths of a right triangle.

Trigonometric Functions in Right Triangles	If θ is the measure of an acute angle of a right triangle, opp is the measure of the leg opposite θ, adj is the measure of the leg adjacent to θ, and hyp is the measure of the hypotenuse, then the following are true.
	$\sin\theta = \dfrac{opp}{hyp} \qquad \cos\theta = \dfrac{adj}{hyp} \qquad \tan\theta = \dfrac{opp}{adj}$ $\csc\theta = \dfrac{hyp}{opp} \qquad \sec\theta = \dfrac{hyp}{adj} \qquad \cot\theta = \dfrac{adj}{opp}$

Example In a right triangle, $\angle B$ is acute and $\cos B = \dfrac{3}{7}$. Find the value of $\tan B$.

Step 1 Draw a right triangle and label one acute angle B. Label the adjacent side 3 and the hypotenuse 7.

Step 2 Use the Pythagorean Theorem to find b.

$a^2 + b^2 = c^2$ Pythagorean Theorem
$3^2 + b^2 = 7^2$ $a = 3$ and $c = 7$
$9 + b^2 = 49$ Simplify.
$b^2 = 40$ Subtract 9 from each side.
$b = \sqrt{40} = 2\sqrt{10}$ Take the positive square root of each side.

Step 3 Find $\tan B$.

$\tan B = \dfrac{opp}{adj}$
$\tan B = \dfrac{2\sqrt{10}}{3}$

Exercises

Find the values of the six trigonometric functions for angle θ.

1.

$\sin\theta = \dfrac{5}{13}$; $\cos\theta = \dfrac{12}{13}$;
$\tan\theta = \dfrac{5}{12}$; $\csc\theta = \dfrac{13}{5}$;
$\sec\theta = \dfrac{13}{12}$; $\cot\theta = \dfrac{12}{5}$

2.

$\sin\theta = \dfrac{4}{5}$; $\cos\theta = \dfrac{3}{5}$;
$\tan\theta = \dfrac{4}{3}$; $\csc\theta = \dfrac{5}{4}$;
$\sec\theta = \dfrac{5}{3}$; $\cot\theta = \dfrac{3}{4}$

3.

$\sin\theta = \dfrac{8}{17}$; $\cos\theta = \dfrac{15}{17}$;
$\tan\theta = \dfrac{8}{15}$; $\csc\theta = \dfrac{17}{8}$;
$\sec\theta = \dfrac{17}{15}$; $\cot\theta = \dfrac{15}{8}$

In a right triangle, $\angle A$ and $\angle B$ are acute.

4. If $\tan A = \dfrac{7}{12}$, what is $\cos A$?
$\dfrac{12\sqrt{193}}{193}$ or ≈ 0.864

5. If $\cos A = \dfrac{1}{2}$, what is $\tan A$?
$\sqrt{3}$ or ≈ 1.732

6. If $\sin B = \dfrac{3}{8}$, what is $\tan B$?
$\dfrac{3\sqrt{55}}{55}$ or ≈ 0.405

Chapter 13   5   Glencoe Algebra 2

Chapter Resources

NAME _____ DATE _____ PERIOD _____

13 Anticipation Guide

Trigonometric Functions

Step 1 *Before you begin Chapter 13*

• Read each statement.
• Decide whether you Agree (A) or Disagree (D) with the statement.
• Write A or D in the first column OR if you are not sure whether you agree or disagree, write NS (Not Sure).

STEP 1 A, D, or NS	Statement	STEP 2 A or D
	1. The tangent of an acute angle in a right triangle is the ratio of the side adjacent to the angle and the side opposite the angle.	D
	2. Solving a triangle means finding the measures of all side lengths and all angles.	A
	3. A radian is the measure of an angle in standard position whose rays intercept an arc length of 1 unit on the unit circle.	A
	4. A reference angle always measures between 90° and 180°.	D
	5. In cases where the Law of Sines can be used to solve a triangle, the Law of Sines always produces a unique solution.	D
	6. The Law of Sines can be used to solve a triangle when two angles and any side of the triangle are given.	A
	7. The Law of Cosines can be used to solve a triangle when all three sides of the triangle are given.	A
	8. The sine and cosine functions each have a period of 180°.	D
	9. The relation represented by $y = \sin^{-1} x$ is not a function, but the relation represented by $y = \operatorname{Sin}^{-1} x$ is a function.	A
	10. An angle is in standard position if it has its vertex at the origin and its initial side is along the positive y-axis.	D

Step 2 *After you complete Chapter 13*

• Reread each statement and complete the last column by entering an A or a D.
• Did any of your opinions about the statements change from the first column?
• For those statements that you mark with a D, use a piece of paper to write an example of why you disagree.

Chapter 13   3   Glencoe Algebra 2

13-1 Skills Practice

Trigonometric Functions in Right Triangles

Find the values of the six trigonometric functions for angle θ.

1.

$\sin \theta = \dfrac{4}{5}$, $\cos \theta = \dfrac{3}{5}$,

$\tan \theta = \dfrac{4}{3}$, $\csc \theta = \dfrac{5}{4}$,

$\sec \theta = \dfrac{5}{3}$, $\cot \theta = \dfrac{3}{4}$

2.

$\sin \theta = \dfrac{5}{13}$, $\cos \theta = \dfrac{12}{13}$,

$\tan \theta = \dfrac{5}{12}$, $\csc \theta = \dfrac{13}{5}$,

$\sec \theta = \dfrac{13}{12}$, $\cot \theta = \dfrac{12}{5}$

3.

$\sin \theta = \dfrac{3\sqrt{13}}{13}$,

$\cos \theta = \dfrac{2\sqrt{13}}{13}$,

$\tan \theta = \dfrac{3}{2}$, $\csc \theta = \dfrac{\sqrt{13}}{3}$,

$\sec \theta = \dfrac{\sqrt{13}}{2}$, $\cot \theta = \dfrac{2}{3}$

In a right triangle, $\angle A$ is acute.

4. If $\tan A = 3$, what is $\sin A$?

$\dfrac{3\sqrt{10}}{10}$ or 0.949

5. If $\sin A = \dfrac{1}{16}$, what is $\cos A$?

$\dfrac{\sqrt{255}}{16}$ or 0.998

Use a trigonometric function to find the value of x. Round to the nearest tenth if necessary.

6. $\tan 30° = \dfrac{8}{x}$; $x \approx 13.9$

7. $\cos 60° = \dfrac{5}{x}$; $x = 10$

8. $\tan 22° = \dfrac{x}{10}$, $x \approx 4.0$

9. $\sin 60° = \dfrac{x}{5}$, $x \approx 4.3$

10. $\cos 51° = \dfrac{x}{8}$; $x \approx 5.0$

11. $\tan 63° = \dfrac{x}{2}$, $x \approx 3.9$

Find the value of x. Round to the nearest tenth if necessary.

12. $x \approx 36.9°$

13. $x \approx 32.6°$

14. $x \approx 82.4°$

13-1 Study Guide and Intervention (continued)

Trigonometric Functions in Right Triangles

Use Trigonometric Functions You can use trigonometric functions to find missing side lengths and missing angle measures of right triangles. You can find the measure of the missing angle by using the inverse of sine, cosine, or tangent.

Example   Find the measure of $\angle C$. Round to the nearest tenth if necessary.

You know the measure of the side opposite $\angle C$ and the measure of the hypotenuse. Use the sine function.

$\sin C = \dfrac{opp}{hyp}$ Sine function

$\sin C = \dfrac{8}{10}$ Replace opp with 8 and hyp with 10.

$\sin^{-1} \dfrac{8}{10} = m\angle C$ Inverse sine

$53.1° \approx m\angle C$ Use a calculator.

Exercises

Use a trigonometric function to find each value of x. Round to the nearest tenth if necessary.

1. $\tan 38° = \dfrac{10}{x}$; 12.8

2. $\cos 63° = \dfrac{4}{x}$; 8.8

3. $\sin 20° = \dfrac{x}{14.5}$; 5.0

4. $\cos 45° = \dfrac{5}{x}$; 7.1

5. $\sin 32° = \dfrac{x}{8}$; 4.2

6. $\tan 70° = \dfrac{9}{x}$; 3.3

Find x. Round to the nearest tenth if necessary.

7. 55.2

8. 66.8

9. 23.6

NAME _____ DATE _____ PERIOD _____

13-1 Practice

Trigonometric Functions in Right Triangles

Find the values of the six trigonometric functions for angle θ.

1.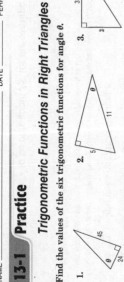

2.

3.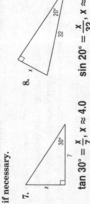

$\sin \theta = \dfrac{15}{17}$, $\cos \theta = \dfrac{8}{17}$,
$\sin \theta = \dfrac{5}{11}$, $\cos \theta = \dfrac{4\sqrt{6}}{11}$,
$\sin \theta = \dfrac{1}{2}$, $\cos \theta = \dfrac{\sqrt{3}}{2}$,

$\tan \theta = \dfrac{15}{8}$, $\csc \theta = \dfrac{17}{15}$,
$\tan \theta = \dfrac{5\sqrt{6}}{24}$, $\csc \theta = \dfrac{11}{5}$,
$\tan \theta = \dfrac{\sqrt{3}}{3}$, $\csc \theta = 2$,

$\sec \theta = \dfrac{17}{8}$, $\cot \theta = \dfrac{8}{15}$
$\sec \theta = \dfrac{11\sqrt{6}}{24}$, $\cot \theta = \dfrac{4\sqrt{6}}{5}$
$\sec \theta = \dfrac{2\sqrt{3}}{3}$, $\cot \theta = \sqrt{3}$

In a right triangle, ∠A and ∠B are acute.

4. If $\tan B = 2$, what is $\cos B$? **0.447**

5. If $\tan A = \dfrac{11}{17}$, what is $\sin A$? **0.543**

6. If $\sin B = \dfrac{8}{15}$, what is $\cos B$? **0.846**

Use a trigonometric function to find each value of x. Round to the nearest tenth if necessary.

7. $\tan 30° = \dfrac{x}{7}$, $x \approx 4.0$

8. $\sin 20° = \dfrac{x}{32}$, $x \approx 10.9$

9. $\tan 49° = \dfrac{17}{x}$, $x \approx 14.8$

Use trigonometric functions to find the values of x and y. Round to the nearest tenth if necessary.

10. $\cos 41° = \dfrac{28}{x}$, $x \approx 37.1$, $\tan x° = \dfrac{19.2}{17}$, $x \approx 48.5$, $\sin x° = \dfrac{7}{15.3}$, $x \approx 27.2$

11. $\tan 41° = \dfrac{y}{28}$, $y \approx 24.3$

12. $\tan y° = \dfrac{17}{19.2}$, $y \approx 41.5$, $\cos y° = \dfrac{7}{15.3}$, $y \approx 62.8$

13. **SURVEYING** John stands 150 meters from a water tower and sights the top at an angle of elevation of 36°. If John's eyes are 2 meters above the ground, how tall is the tower? Round to the nearest meter. **111 m**

NAME _____ DATE _____ PERIOD _____

13-1 Word Problem Practice

Trigonometric Functions in Right Triangles

1. **ROOFS** The roof on a house is built with a pitch of 10/12, meaning that the roof rises 10 feet for every 12 feet of horizontal run. The side view of the roof is shown in the figure below.

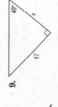

a. What is the angle x at the base of the roof? **≈ 39.8°**

b. What is the angle y at the peak of the roof? **≈ 100.4°**

c. What is the length ℓ of the roof? **≈ 15.6 ft**

d. If the width of the roof is 26 feet, what is the total area of the roof? **≈ 812.3 ft²**

2. **BUILDINGS** Jessica stands 150 feet from the base of a tall building. She measures the angle from her eye to the top of the building to be 84°. If her eye level is 5 feet above the ground, how tall is the building? **≈ 1427 ft**

3. **SCALE DRAWING** The collection pool for a fountain is in the shape of a right triangle. A scale drawing shows that the angles of the triangle are 40°, 50°, and 90°. If the hypotenuse of the actual fountain will be 30 feet, what are the lengths of the other two sides of the fountain? **about 19.3 ft and 23.0 ft**

4. **GEOMETRY** A regular hexagon is inscribed in a circle with a diameter of 8 inches.

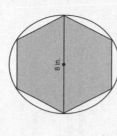

a. What is the perimeter of the hexagon? **24 in.**

b. What is the area of the hexagon? **$24\sqrt{3}$ or about 41.6 in²**

NAME _____ DATE _____ PERIOD _____

13-2 Study Guide and Intervention

Angles and Angle Measure

Angles in Standard Position An angle is determined by two rays. The degree measure of an angle in standard position is described by the amount and direction of rotation from the **initial side**, which lies along the positive x-axis, to the **terminal side**. A counterclockwise rotation is associated with positive angle measure and a clockwise rotation is associated with negative angle measure. Two or more angles in standard position with the same terminal side are called **coterminal angles**.

Example 1 Draw an angle with measure 290° in standard position.

The negative y-axis represents a positive rotation of 270°. To generate an angle of 290°, rotate the terminal side 20° more in the counterclockwise direction

Example 2 Find an angle with a positive measure and an angle with a negative measure that are coterminal with each angle.

a. **250°**
A positive angle is 250° + 360° or 610°.   Add 360°.
A negative angle is 250° − 360° or −110°.   Subtract 360°.

b. **−140°**
A positive angle is −140° + 360° or 220°.   Add 360°.
A negative angle is −140° − 360° or −500°. Subtract 360°.

Exercises

Draw an angle with the given measure in standard position.

1. 160°

2. 280°

3. 400°

Find an angle with a positive measure and an angle with a negative measure that are coterminal with each angle.

4. 65° **425°, −295°**

5. −75° **285°, −435°**

6. 230° **590°, −130°**

7. 420° **60°, −300°**

NAME _____ DATE _____ PERIOD _____

13-1 Enrichment

The Angle of Repose

Suppose you place a block of wood on an inclined plane, as shown at the right. If the angle, θ, at which the plane is inclined from the horizontal is very small, the block will not move. If you increase the angle, the block will eventually overcome the force of friction and start to slide down the plane.

At the instant the block begins to slide, the angle formed by the plane is called the angle of friction, or the angle of repose.

For situations in which the block and plane are smooth but unlubricated, the angle of repose depends *only* on the types of materials in the block and the plane. The angle is independent of the area of contact between the two surfaces and of the weight of the block.

The drawing at the right shows how to use vectors to find a coefficient of friction. This coefficient varies with different materials and is denoted by the Greek letter mu, μ.

$$F = W \sin \theta \qquad N = W \cos \theta$$
$$F = \mu N$$
$$\mu = \frac{\sin \theta}{\cos \theta} = \tan \theta$$

Material	Coefficient of Friction μ
Wood on wood	0.5
Wood on stone	0.5
Rubber tire on dry concrete	1.0
Rubber tire on wet concrete	0.7

Solve each problem.

1. A wooden chute is built so that wooden crates can slide down into the basement of a store. What angle should the chute make in order for the crates to slide down at a constant speed?
≈ 26.6°

2. Will a 100-pound wooden crate slide down a stone ramp that makes an angle of 20° with the horizontal? Explain your answer.
No, the angle must be at least 26.6°.

3. If you increase the weight of the crate in Exercise 2 to 300 pounds, does it change your answer?
No, the weight does not affect the angle.

4. A car with rubber tires is being driven on dry concrete pavement. If the car tires spin without traction on a hill, how steep is the hill?
at least 45°

5. For Exercise 4, does it make a difference if it starts to rain? Explain your answer.
Yes, the street needs to be only about 35° for the car tires to spin.

Left page (Study Guide and Intervention):

NAME _____ DATE _____ PERIOD _____

13-2 Study Guide and Intervention *(continued)*

Angles and Angle Measure

Convert Between Degrees and Radians Angles can be measured in degrees and radians, which are units based on arc length. One radian is the measure of an angle θ in standard position with a terminal side that intercepts an arc with the same length as the radius of the circle. Degree measure and radian measure are related by the equations 2π radians = $360°$ and π radians = $180°$.

Radian and Degree Measure	To rewrite the radian measure of an angle in degrees, multiply the number of radians by $\dfrac{180°}{\pi \text{ radians}}$.
	To rewrite the degree measure of an angle in radians, multiply the number of degrees by $\dfrac{\pi \text{ radians}}{180°}$.
Arc Length	For a circle with radius r and central angle θ(in radians), the arc length s equals the product of r and θ. $s = r\theta$

Example 1 Rewrite each degree measure in radians and the radian measure in degrees.

a. $45°$
$45° = 45° \left(\dfrac{\pi \text{ radians}}{180°} \right) = \dfrac{\pi}{4}$ radians

b. $\dfrac{5\pi}{3}$ radians
$\dfrac{5\pi}{3}$ radians $= \dfrac{5\pi}{3} \left(\dfrac{180°}{\pi} \right) = 300°$

Example 2 A circle has a radius of 5 cm and central angle of 135°, what is the length of the circle's arc?

Find the central angle in radians.
$135° = 135° \left(\dfrac{\pi \text{ radians}}{180°} \right) = \dfrac{3\pi}{4}$ radians

Use the radius and central angle to find the arc length.
$s = r\theta$ Write the formula for arc length.
$= 5 \cdot \dfrac{3\pi}{4}$ Replace r with 5 and θ with $\dfrac{3\pi}{4}$.
≈ 11.78 Use a calculator to simplify.

Exercises

Rewrite each degree measure in radians and each radian measure in degrees.

1. $140°$ 2. $-260°$ 3. $-\dfrac{3\pi}{5}$
$\dfrac{7\pi}{9}$ $-\dfrac{13\pi}{9}$ $-108°$

4. $-75°$ 5. $\dfrac{7\pi}{6}$ 6. $380°$
$-\dfrac{5\pi}{12}$ $210°$ $\dfrac{19\pi}{9}$

Find the length of each arc. Round to the nearest tenth.

7.

8.

9.

8.4 units   11.0 units   12.6 units

Right page (Skills Practice):

NAME _____ DATE _____ PERIOD _____

13-2 Skills Practice

Angles and Angle Measure

Draw an angle with the given measure in standard position.

1. $185°$ 2. $810°$ 3. $390°$

4. $495°$ 5. $-50°$ 6. $-420°$

Find an angle with a positive measure and an angle with a negative measure that are coterminal with each angle. 7–14. Sample answers are given.

7. $45°$ $405°, -315°$ 8. $60°$ $420°, -300°$

9. $370°$ $10°, -350°$ 10. $-90°$ $270°, -450°$

11. $\dfrac{2\pi}{3}$ $\dfrac{8\pi}{3}, -\dfrac{4\pi}{3}$ 12. $\dfrac{5\pi}{2}$ $\dfrac{9\pi}{2}, -\dfrac{3\pi}{2}$

13. $\dfrac{\pi}{6}$ $\dfrac{13\pi}{6}, -\dfrac{11\pi}{6}$ 14. $-\dfrac{3\pi}{4}$ $\dfrac{5\pi}{4}, -\dfrac{11\pi}{4}$

Rewrite each degree measure in radians and each radian measure in degrees.

15. $-30°$ $-\dfrac{\pi}{6}$ 16. $720°$ 4π

17. $-10°$ $-\dfrac{\pi}{18}$ 18. $90°$ $\dfrac{\pi}{2}$

19. $-30°$ $-\dfrac{\pi}{6}$ 20. $-270°$ $-\dfrac{3\pi}{2}$

21. $\dfrac{\pi}{3}$ $60°$ 22. $\dfrac{5\pi}{6}$ $150°$

23. $\dfrac{2\pi}{3}$ $120°$ 24. $\dfrac{5\pi}{4}$ $225°$

25. $-\dfrac{3\pi}{4}$ $-135°$ 26. $-\dfrac{7\pi}{6}$ $-210°$

Answers (Lesson 13-2)

13-2 Word Problem Practice

Angles and Angle Measure

1. AMUSEMENT PARKS The carousel at an amusement park has 20 horses spaced evenly around its circumference. The horses are numbered consecutively from 1 to 20. The carousel completes one rotation about its axis every 40 seconds.

a. What is the central angle, in degrees, formed by horse #1 and horse #8?

126°

b. What is the speed of the carousel in rotations per minute?

1.5 rotations per minute

c. What is the speed of the carousel in radians per minute?

3π radians per minute

d. A child rides the carousel for 6 minutes. Through how many radians will the child pass in the course of the carousel ride?

18π radians

2. TIME Through what angle, in degrees and radians, does the hour hand on a clock rotate between 4 P.M. and 7 P.M.? Assuming the length of the hour hand is 6 inches, find the arc length of the circle made by the hour hand during that time.

90°, $\frac{\pi}{2}$ radians; 3π inches

3. TIME Through what angle, in degrees and radians, does the minute hand rotate between 4 P.M. and 7 P.M.?

1080°, 6π radians

4. PLANETS Earth makes one full rotation on its axis every 24 hours. How long does it take Earth to rotate through 150°? Neptune makes one full rotation on its axis every 16 hours. How long does it take Neptune to rotate through 150°?

10 hours, $6\frac{2}{3}$ hours

13-2 Practice

Angles and Angle Measure

Draw an angle with the given measure in standard position.

1. 210°

2. 305°

3. 580°

4. 135°

5. −450°

6. −560°

Find an angle with a positive measure and an angle with a negative measure that are coterminal with each angle.

7. 65° **425°, −295°**

8. 80° **440°, −280°**

9. 110° **470°, −250°**

10. $\frac{2\pi}{5}$ **$\frac{12\pi}{5}$, $-\frac{8\pi}{5}$**

11. $\frac{5\pi}{6}$ **$\frac{17\pi}{6}$, $-\frac{7\pi}{6}$**

12. $-\frac{3\pi}{2}$ **$\frac{\pi}{2}$, $-\frac{7\pi}{2}$**

Rewrite each degree measure in radians and each radian measure in degrees.

13. 18° **$\frac{\pi}{10}$**

14. 6° **$\frac{\pi}{30}$**

15. −72° **$-\frac{2\pi}{5}$**

16. −820° **$-\frac{41\pi}{9}$**

17. 4π **720°**

18. $\frac{5\pi}{2}$ **450°**

19. $-\frac{9\pi}{2}$ **−810°**

20. $-\frac{7\pi}{12}$ **−105°**

Find the length of each arc. Round to the nearest tenth.

21.

5.5 units

22.

20.0 units

23.
29.4 units

24. **TIME** Find both the degree and radian measures of the angle through which the hour hand on a clock rotates from 5 A.M. to 10 P.M.

−510°; $-\frac{17\pi}{6}$

25. **ROTATION** A truck with 16-inch radius wheels is driven at 77 feet per second (52.5 miles per hour). Find the measure of the angle through which a point on the outside of the wheel travels each second. Round to the nearest degree and nearest radian.

3309°/s; 58 radians/s

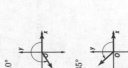

Answers (Lesson 13-2 and Lesson 13-3)

NAME _____ DATE _____ PERIOD _____

13-2 Enrichment

Making and Using a Hypsometer

A **hypsometer** is a device that can be used to measure the height of an object. To construct your own hypsometer, you will need a rectangular piece of heavy cardboard that is at least 7 cm by 10 cm, a straw, transparent tape, a string about 20 cm long, and a small weight that can be attached to the string.

Mark off 1-cm increments along one short side and one long side of the cardboard. Tape the straw to the other short side. Then attach the weight to one end of the string, and attach the other end of the string to one corner of the cardboard, as shown in the figure below. The diagram below shows how your hypsometer should look.

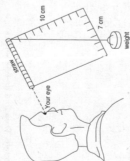

To use the hypsometer, you will need to measure the distance from the base of the object whose height you are finding to where you stand when you use the hypsometer.

Sight the top of the object through the straw. Note where the free-hanging string crosses the bottom scale. Then use similar triangles to find the height of the object.

1. Draw a diagram to illustrate how you can use similar triangles and the hypsometer to find the height of a tall object. **See students' diagrams.**

Use your hypsometer to find the height of each of the following. **2–6. See students' work.**

2. your school's flagpole

3. a tree on your school's property

4. the highest point on the front wall of your school building

5. the goal posts on a football field

6. the hoop on a basketball court

Chapter 13   16   Glencoe Algebra 2

NAME _____ DATE _____ PERIOD _____

13-3 Study Guide and Intervention

Trigonometric Functions of General Angles

Trigonometric Functions for General Angles

Trigonometric Functions, θ in Standard Position	Let θ be an angle in standard position and let $P(x, y)$ be a point on the terminal side of θ. By the Pythagorean Theorem, the distance r from the origin is given by $r = \sqrt{x^2 + y^2}$. The trigonometric functions of an angle in standard position may be defined as follows.

$$\sin \theta = \frac{y}{r} \qquad \cos \theta = \frac{x}{r} \qquad \tan \theta = \frac{y}{x}, x \neq 0$$

$$\csc \theta = \frac{r}{y}, y \neq 0 \qquad \sec \theta = \frac{r}{x}, x \neq 0 \qquad \cot \theta = \frac{x}{y}, y \neq 0$$

Example Find the exact values of the six trigonometric functions of θ if the terminal side of θ in standard position contains the point $(-5, 5\sqrt{2})$.

You know that $x = -5$ and $y = 5$. You need to find r.

$r = \sqrt{x^2 + y^2}$ Pythagorean Theorem

$ = \sqrt{(-5)^2 + (5\sqrt{2})^2}$ Replace x with -5 and y with $5\sqrt{2}$.

$ = \sqrt{75}$ or $5\sqrt{3}$

Now use $x = -5$, $y = 5\sqrt{2}$, and $r = 5\sqrt{3}$ to write the six trigonometric ratios.

$\sin \theta = \frac{y}{r} = \frac{5\sqrt{2}}{5\sqrt{3}} = \frac{\sqrt{6}}{3}$ $\cos \theta = \frac{x}{r} = \frac{-5}{5\sqrt{3}} = -\frac{\sqrt{3}}{3}$ $\tan \theta = \frac{y}{x} = \frac{5\sqrt{2}}{-5} = -\sqrt{2}$

$\csc \theta = \frac{r}{y} = \frac{5\sqrt{3}}{5\sqrt{2}} = \frac{\sqrt{6}}{2}$ $\sec \theta = \frac{r}{x} = \frac{5\sqrt{3}}{-5} = -\sqrt{3}$ $\cot \theta = \frac{x}{y} = \frac{-5}{5\sqrt{2}} = -\frac{\sqrt{2}}{2}$

Exercises

The terminal side of θ in standard position contains each point. Find the exact values of the six trigonometric functions of θ.

1. $(-8, 4)$

$\sin \theta = \frac{\sqrt{5}}{5}$, $\cos \theta = \frac{2\sqrt{5}}{5}$, $\tan \theta$ $= -\frac{1}{2}$, $\csc \theta = \sqrt{5}$, $\sec \theta = \frac{\sqrt{5}}{2}$, $\cot \theta = 2$

2. $(4, 4)$

$\sin \theta = \frac{\sqrt{2}}{2}$, $\cos \theta = \frac{\sqrt{2}}{2}$, $\tan \theta = 1$, $\csc \theta = \sqrt{2}$, $\sec \theta = \sqrt{2}$, $\cot \theta = 1$

3. $(0, 4)$

$\sin \theta = 1$, $\cos \theta = 0$, $\tan \theta = $ undefined, $\csc \theta = 1$, $\sec \theta = $ undefined, $\cot \theta = 0$

4. $(6, 2)$

$\sin \theta = \frac{\sqrt{10}}{10}$, $\cos \theta = \frac{3\sqrt{10}}{10}$, $\tan \theta = \frac{1}{3}$, $\csc \theta = \sqrt{10}$, $\sec \theta = \frac{\sqrt{10}}{3}$, $\cot \theta = 3$

Chapter 13   17   Glencoe Algebra 2

Answers (Lesson 13-3)

13-3 Skills Practice

Trigonometric Functions of General Angles

The terminal side of θ in standard position contains each point. Find the exact values of the six trigonometric functions of θ.

1. (5, 12)
$\sin \theta = \dfrac{12}{13}$, $\cos \theta = \dfrac{5}{13}$, $\tan \theta = \dfrac{12}{5}$
$\csc \theta = \dfrac{13}{12}$, $\sec \theta = \dfrac{13}{5}$, $\cot \theta = \dfrac{5}{12}$

2. (3, 4)
$\sin \theta = \dfrac{4}{5}$, $\cos \theta = \dfrac{3}{5}$, $\tan \theta = \dfrac{4}{3}$
$\csc \theta = \dfrac{5}{4}$, $\sec \theta = \dfrac{5}{3}$, $\cot \theta = \dfrac{3}{4}$

3. (8, -15)
$\sin \theta = -\dfrac{15}{17}$, $\cos \theta = \dfrac{8}{17}$, $\tan \theta = -\dfrac{15}{8}$
$\csc \theta = -\dfrac{17}{15}$, $\sec \theta = \dfrac{17}{8}$, $\cot \theta = -\dfrac{8}{15}$

4. (-4, 3)
$\sin \theta = \dfrac{3}{5}$, $\cos \theta = -\dfrac{4}{5}$, $\tan \theta = -\dfrac{3}{4}$
$\csc \theta = \dfrac{5}{3}$, $\sec \theta = -\dfrac{5}{4}$, $\cot \theta = -\dfrac{4}{3}$

5. (-9, -40)
$\sin \theta = -\dfrac{40}{41}$, $\cos \theta = -\dfrac{9}{41}$, $\tan \theta = \dfrac{40}{9}$
$\csc \theta = -\dfrac{41}{40}$, $\sec \theta = -\dfrac{41}{9}$, $\cot \theta = \dfrac{9}{40}$

6. (1, 2)
$\sin \theta = \dfrac{2\sqrt{5}}{5}$, $\cos \theta = \dfrac{\sqrt{5}}{5}$, $\tan \theta = 2$
$\csc \theta = \dfrac{\sqrt{5}}{2}$, $\sec \theta = \sqrt{5}$, $\cot \theta = \dfrac{1}{2}$

7. (3, -9)
$\sin \theta = -\dfrac{3\sqrt{10}}{10}$, $\cos \theta = \dfrac{\sqrt{10}}{10}$, $\tan \theta = -3$
$\csc \theta = -\dfrac{\sqrt{10}}{3}$, $\sec \theta = \dfrac{\sqrt{10}}{1}$, $\cot \theta = -\dfrac{1}{3}$

8. (-8, 12)
$\sin \theta = \dfrac{3\sqrt{13}}{13}$, $\cos \theta = -\dfrac{2\sqrt{13}}{13}$, $\tan \theta = -\dfrac{3}{2}$
$\csc \theta = \dfrac{\sqrt{13}}{3}$, $\sec \theta = -\dfrac{\sqrt{13}}{2}$, $\cot \theta = -\dfrac{2}{3}$

Sketch each angle. Then find its reference angle.

9. 135° **45°**
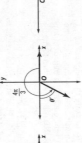

10. 200° **20°**

11. $\dfrac{5\pi}{3}$ $\dfrac{\pi}{3}$

Find the exact value of each trigonometric function.

12. $\sin 150°$ $\dfrac{1}{2}$

13. $\cos 270°$ **0**

14. $\cot 135°$ **-1**

15. $\tan (-30°)$ $-\dfrac{\sqrt{3}}{3}$

16. $\tan \dfrac{\pi}{4}$ **1**

17. $\cos \dfrac{4\pi}{3}$ $-\dfrac{1}{2}$

18. $\cot (-\pi)$ **undefined**

19. $\sin \left(-\dfrac{3\pi}{4}\right)$ $-\dfrac{\sqrt{2}}{2}$

13-3 Study Guide and Intervention (continued)

Trigonometric Functions of General Angles

Trigonometric Functions with Reference Angles If θ is a nonquadrantal angle in standard position, its reference angle θ' is defined as the acute angle formed by the terminal side of θ and the x-axis.

Reference Angle Rule			
Quadrant I	Quadrant II	Quadrant III	Quadrant IV
$\theta' = \theta$	$\theta' = 180° - \theta$ ($\theta' = \pi - \theta$)	$\theta' = \theta - 180°$ ($\theta' = \theta - \pi$)	$\theta' = 360° - \theta$ ($\theta' = 2\pi - \theta$)

Example 1   Sketch an angle of measure 205°. Then find its reference angle.

Because the terminal side of 205° lies in Quadrant III, the reference angle θ' is $205° - 180°$ or $25°$.

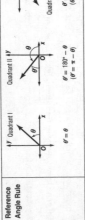

Example 2   Use a reference angle to find the exact value of $\cos \dfrac{3\pi}{4}$.

Because the terminal side of $\dfrac{3\pi}{4}$ lies in Quadrant II, the reference angle θ' is
$\pi - \dfrac{3\pi}{4}$ or $\dfrac{\pi}{4}$.
The cosine function is negative in Quadrant II.
$\cos \dfrac{3\pi}{4} = -\cos \dfrac{\pi}{4} = -\dfrac{\sqrt{2}}{2}$

Exercises

Sketch each angle. Then find its reference angle.

1. 155° **25°**

2. 230° **50°**

3. $\dfrac{4\pi}{3}$ $\dfrac{\pi}{3}$

4. $-\dfrac{\pi}{6}$ $\dfrac{\pi}{6}$
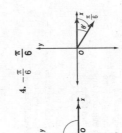

Find the exact value of each trigonometric function.

5. $\tan 330°$ $-\dfrac{\sqrt{3}}{3}$

6. $\cos \dfrac{11\pi}{4}$ $-\dfrac{\sqrt{2}}{2}$

7. $\cot 30°$ $\sqrt{3}$

8. $\csc \dfrac{\pi}{4}$ $\sqrt{2}$

13-3 Practice

Trigonometric Functions of General Angles

The terminal side of θ in standard position contains each point. Find the exact values of the six trigonometric functions of θ.

1. (6, 8)
$\sin \theta = \dfrac{4}{5}$, $\cos \theta = \dfrac{3}{5}$,
$\tan \theta = \dfrac{4}{3}$, $\csc \theta = \dfrac{5}{4}$,
$\sec \theta = \dfrac{5}{3}$, $\cot \theta = \dfrac{3}{4}$

2. (-20, 21)
$\sin \theta = \dfrac{21}{29}$, $\cos \theta = -\dfrac{20}{29}$,
$\tan \theta = -\dfrac{21}{20}$, $\csc \theta = \dfrac{29}{21}$,
$\sec \theta = -\dfrac{29}{20}$, $\cot \theta = -\dfrac{20}{21}$

3. (-2, -5)
$\sin \theta = -\dfrac{5\sqrt{29}}{29}$, $\cos \theta = -\dfrac{2\sqrt{29}}{29}$,
$\tan \theta = \dfrac{5}{2}$, $\csc \theta = -\dfrac{\sqrt{29}}{5}$,
$\sec \theta = -\dfrac{\sqrt{29}}{2}$, $\cot \theta = \dfrac{2}{5}$

Sketch each angle. Then find its reference angle.

4. $\dfrac{13\pi}{8}$ $\dfrac{3\pi}{8}$

5. $-210°$ $30°$

6. $-\dfrac{7\pi}{4}$ $\dfrac{\pi}{4}$

Find the exact value of each trigonometric function.

7. $\tan 135°$ $\;-1$

8. $\cot 210°$ $\;\sqrt{3}$

9. $\cot (-90°)$ $\;0$

10. $\cos 405°$ $\;\dfrac{\sqrt{2}}{2}$

11. $\tan \dfrac{5\pi}{3}$ $\;-\sqrt{3}$

12. $\csc\left(-\dfrac{3\pi}{4}\right)$ $\;-\sqrt{2}$

13. $\cot 2\pi$ $\;$undefined

14. $\tan \dfrac{13\pi}{6}$ $\;\dfrac{\sqrt{3}}{3}$

15. **LIGHT** Light rays that "bounce off" a surface are *reflected* by the surface. If the surface is partially transparent, some of the light rays are bent or *refracted* as they pass from the air through the material. The angles of reflection θ_1 and of refraction θ_2 in the diagram at the right are related by the equation $\sin \theta_1 = n \sin \theta_2$. If $\theta_1 = 60°$ and $n = \sqrt{3}$, find the measure of θ_2. **30°**

16. **FORCE** A cable running from the top of a utility pole to the ground exerts a horizontal pull of 800 Newtons and a vertical pull of $800\sqrt{3}$ Newtons. What is the sine of the angle θ between the cable and the ground? What is the measure of this angle? $\dfrac{\sqrt{3}}{2}$; **60°**

13-3 Word Problem Practice

Trigonometric Functions of General Angles

1. **RADIOS** Two correspondence radios are located 2 kilometers away from a base camp. The angle formed between the first radio, the base camp, and the second radio is 120°. If the first radio has coordinates (2, 0) relative to the base camp, what is the position of the second radio relative to the base camp? **-1, $\sqrt{3}$**

2. **CLOCKS** The pendulum of a grandfather clock swings back and forth through an arc. The angle θ of the pendulum is given by $\theta = 0.3 \cos\left(\dfrac{\pi}{2} + 5t\right)$ where t is the time in seconds after leaving the bottom of the swing. Determine the measure of the angles in radians for $t = 0$, 0.5, 1, 1.5, 2, 2.5, and 3 seconds.
0, -0.18, 0.28, -0.28, 0.16, 0.02, -0.20

3. **FERRIS WHEELS** Janice rides a Ferris wheel in Japan called the Sky Dream Fukuoka, which has a radius of about 60 m and is 5 m off the ground. After she enters the bottom car, the wheel rotates 210.5° counterclockwise before stopping. How high above the ground is Janice when the car has stopped? **about 116.7 m**

4. **SOCCER** Alice kicks a soccer ball towards a wall. The ball is deflected off the wall at an angle of 40°, and it travels 6 meters. How far is the soccer ball from the wall when it stops rolling? **3.9 m**

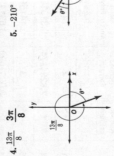

5. **PAPER AIRPLANES** The formula $R = \dfrac{V_0^2 \sin 2\theta}{32} + 15 \cos \theta$ gives the distance traveled by a paper airplane that is thrown with an initial velocity of V_0 feet per second at an angle of θ with the ground.

a. If the airplane is thrown with an initial velocity of 15 feet per second at an angle of 25°, how far will the airplane travel? **19 ft**

b. Two airplanes are thrown with an initial velocity of 10 feet per second. One airplane is thrown at an angle of 15° to the ground, and the other airplane is thrown at an angle of 45° to the ground. Which will travel farther? **The airplane thrown at 15° will travel farther.**

Answers (Lesson 13-3 and Lesson 13-4)

13-4 Study Guide and Intervention

Law of Sines

Find the Area of a Triangle The area of any triangle is one half the product of the lengths of two sides and the sine of the included angle.

Area of a Triangle	area $= \frac{1}{2}bc \sin A$
	area $= \frac{1}{2}ac \sin B$
	area $= \frac{1}{2}ab \sin C$

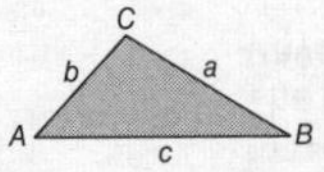

Example **Find the area of $\triangle ABC$ to the nearest tenth.**

In $\triangle ABC$, $a = 10$, $b = 14$, and $C = 40°$.

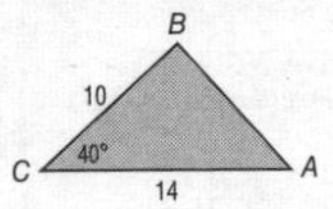

Area $= \frac{1}{2}ab \sin C$ Area formula

  $= \frac{1}{2}(10)(14)\sin 40°$ Substitution

  ≈ 44.9951 Simplify.

The area of the triangle is approximately 45 square units.

Exercises

Find the area of $\triangle ABC$ to the nearest tenth, if necessary.

1.

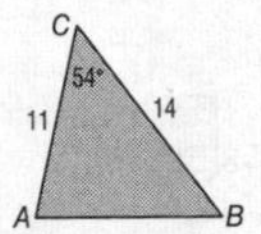

62.3 units²

2.

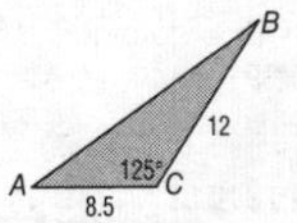

41.8 units²

3.

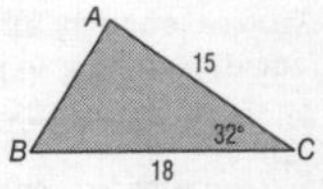

71.5 units²

4.

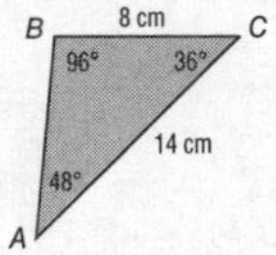

32.9 cm²

5.

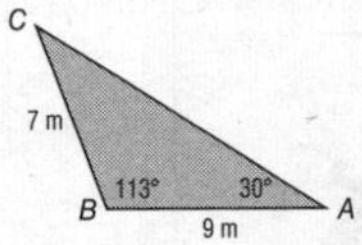

29.0 m²

6.

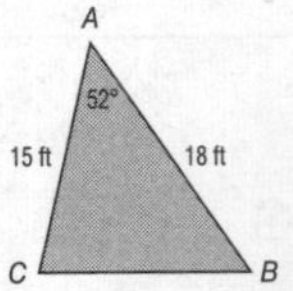

106.4 ft²

7. $A = 20°$, $c = 4$ cm, $b = 7$ cm   **4.8 cm²**

8. $C = 55°$, $a = 10$ m, $b = 15$ m   **61.4 m²**

9. $B = 42°$, $c = 9$ ft, $a = 3$ ft   **9.0 ft²**

10. $c = 15$ in, $b = 13$ in, $A = 53°$ **77.9 in²**

11. $a = 12$ cm, $b = 8$ cm, $C = 85°$ **47.8 cm²**

13-3 Enrichment

Areas of Polygons and Circles

A regular polygon has sides of equal length and angles of equal measure. A regular polygon can be inscribed in or circumscribed about a circle. For n-sided regular polygons, the following area formulas can be used.

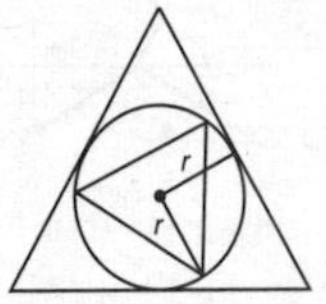

Area of circle $A_c = \pi r^2$

Area of inscribed polygon $A_I = \frac{nr^2}{2} \times \sin \frac{360°}{n}$

Area of circumscribed polygon $A_C = nr^2 \times \tan \frac{180°}{n}$

Use a calculator to complete the chart below for a unit circle (a circle of radius 1).

	Number of Sides	Area of Inscribed Polygon	Area of Circle minus Area of Polygon	Area of Circumscribed Polygon	Area of Polygon minus Area of Circle
	3	1.2990381	1.8425545	5.1961524	2.054598
1.	4	**2**	**1.1415927**	**4**	**0.8584073**
2.	8	**2.8284271**	**0.3131655**	**3.3137085**	**0.1721158**
3.	12	**3**	**0.1415926**	**3.2153903**	**0.0737977**
4.	20	**3.0901699**	**0.0514227**	**3.1676888**	**0.0260962**
5.	24	**3.1058285**	**0.0357641**	**3.1596599**	**0.0180673**
6.	28	**3.1152931**	**0.0262996**	**3.1548423**	**0.0132497**
7.	32	**3.1214452**	**0.0201475**	**3.1517249**	**0.0101323**
8.	1000	**3.1415720**	**0.0000206**	**3.1416030**	**0.0000103**

9. What number do the areas of the circumscribed and inscribed polygons seem to be approaching? **π**

NAME _____ DATE _____ PERIOD _____

13-4 Skills Practice

Law of Sines

Find the area of △ABC to the nearest tenth, if necessary.

1.  **19.0 cm²**

2.  **10.0 ft²**

3. $A = 35°, b = 3$ ft, $c = 7$ ft **6.0 ft²**

4. $C = 148°, a = 10$ cm, $b = 7$ cm **18.5 cm²**

5. $C = 22°, a = 14$ m, $b = 8$ m **21.0 m²**

6. $B = 93°, c = 18$ mi, $a = 42$ mi **377.5 mi²**

Solve each triangle. Round side lengths to the nearest tenth and angle measures to the nearest degree.

7. $B = 93°, a ≈ 102.1,$ $b ≈ 393.8$

8. $B ≈ 29°, C ≈ 30°,$ $c ≈ 123.7$

9. $B ≈ 65°, C ≈ 45°,$ $c ≈ 82.2$

10. $B = 60°, C = 90°,$ $b ≈ 17.3$

11. $C = 150°, a ≈ 31.5,$ $b ≈ 21.2$

12. $C = 68°, a ≈ 14.3,$ $b ≈ 22.9$

Determine whether each triangle has *no solution*, *one solution*, or *two solutions*. Then solve the triangle. Round side lengths to the nearest tenth and angle measures to the nearest degree.

13. $A = 30°, a = 1, b = 4$ **no solution**

14. $A = 30°, a = 2, b = 4$ **one solution;** $B = 90°, C = 60°, c ≈ 3.5$

15. $A = 30°, a = 3, b = 4$ **two solutions;** $B ≈ 42°, C ≈ 108°, c ≈ 5.7;$ $B ≈ 138°, C ≈ 12°, c ≈ 1.2$

16. $A = 38°, a = 10, b = 9$ **one solution;** $B ≈ 34°, C ≈ 108°, c ≈ 15.4$

17. $A = 78°, a = 8, b = 5$ **one solution;** $B ≈ 38°, C ≈ 64°, c ≈ 7.4$

18. $A = 133°, a = 9, b = 7$ **one solution;** $B ≈ 35°, C ≈ 12°, c ≈ 2.6$

19. $A = 127°, a = 2, b = 6$ **no solution**

20. $A = 109°, a = 24, b = 13$ **one solution;** $B ≈ 31°, C ≈ 40°, c ≈ 16.4$

Chapter 13   25   Glencoe Algebra 2

NAME _____ DATE _____ PERIOD _____

13-4 Study Guide and Intervention (continued)

Law of Sines

Use the Law of Sines to Solve Triangles You can use the Law of Sines to solve any triangle if you know the measures of two angles and any side opposite one of the angles, or the measures of two sides and the angle opposite one of them.

Law of Sines	$\dfrac{\sin A}{a} = \dfrac{\sin B}{b} = \dfrac{\sin C}{c}$
Possible Triangles Given Two Sides and One Opposite Angle	Suppose you are given a, b, and A for a triangle.

If a is acute:
$a < b \sin A$ ⇒ no solution
$a = b \sin A$ ⇒ one solution
$b > a > b \sin A$ ⇒ two solutions
$a > b$ ⇒ one solution

If A is right or obtuse:
$a ≤ b$ ⇒ no solution
$a > b$ ⇒ one solution

Example Determine whether △ABC has *no solutions*, *one solution*, or *two solutions*. Then solve △ABC.

a. $A = 48°, a = 11$, and $b = 16$ Since A is acute, find $b \sin A$ and compare it with a. $b \sin A = 16 \sin 48° ≈ 11.89$ Since $11 < 11.89$, there is no solution.

b. $A = 34°, a = 6, b = 8$
Since A is acute, find $b \sin A$ and compare it with a; $b \sin A = 8 \sin 34° ≈ 4.47$. Since $8 > 6 > 4.47$, there are two solutions. Thus there are two possible triangles to solve.

Acute B
First use the Law of Sines to find B.
$$\frac{\sin B}{8} = \frac{\sin 34°}{6}$$
$$\sin B = 0.7456$$
$$B ≈ 48°$$
The measure of angle C is about $180° − (34° + 48°)$ or about $98°$.
Use the Law of Sines again to find c.
$$\frac{\sin 98°}{c} = \frac{\sin 34°}{6}$$
$$c = \frac{6 \sin 98°}{\sin 34°}$$
$$c ≈ 10.6$$

Obtuse B
To find B you need to find an obtuse angle whose sine is also 0.7456.
To do this, subtract the angle given by your calculator, 48°, from 180°. So B is approximately 132°.
The measure of angle C is about $180° − (34° + 132°)$ or about $14°$.
Use the Law of Sines to find c.
$$\frac{\sin 14°}{c} = \frac{\sin 34°}{6}$$
$$c = \frac{6 \sin 14°}{\sin 34°}$$
$$c ≈ 2.6$$

Exercises

Determine whether each triangle has *no solution*, *one solution*, or *two solutions*. Then solve each triangle. Round side lengths to the nearest tenth and angle measures to the nearest degree.

1. $A = 50°, a = 34, b = 40$ **two solutions;** $B ≈ 64°, C ≈ 66°,$ $c ≈ 40.4; B ≈ 116°,$ $C ≈ 14°, c ≈ 11.0$

2. $A = 24°, a = 3, b = 8$ **no solution**

3. $A = 125°, a = 22, b = 15$ **one solution;** $B ≈ 34°, C ≈ 21°,$ $c ≈ 9.6$

Chapter 13   24   Glencoe Algebra 2

Page 26 (Practice)

13-4 Practice

Law of Sines

Find the area of $\triangle ABC$ to the nearest tenth, if necessary.

1.
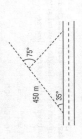

35.6 yd²

2.

29.7 m²

3.

26.0 cm²

4. $C = 32°$, $a = 12.6$ m, $b = 8.9$ m
76.3 m²

5. $B = 27°$, $a = 14.9$ cm, $c = 18.6$ cm
62.9 cm²

6. $A = 17.4°$, $b = 12$ km, $c = 14$ km
25.1 km²

7. $A = 34°$, $b = 19.4$ ft, $c = 8.6$ ft
46.6 ft²

Solve each triangle. Round side lengths to the nearest tenth and angle measures to the nearest degree.

8. $A = 50°$, $B = 30°$, $c = 9$
$C \approx 100°$, $a \approx 7.0$, $b \approx 4.6$

9. $A = 56°$, $B = 38°$, $a = 12$
$C \approx 86°$, $b \approx 8.9$, $c \approx 14.4$

10. $A = 80°$, $C = 14°$, $a = 40$
$B \approx 86°$, $b \approx 40.5$, $c \approx 9.8$

11. $B = 47°$, $C = 112°$, $b = 13$
$A \approx 21°$, $a \approx 6.4$, $c \approx 16.5$

12. $A = 72°$, $a = 8$, $c = 6$
$B \approx 62°$, $C \approx 46°$, $b \approx 7.5$

13. $A = 25°$, $C = 107°$, $b = 12$
$B \approx 48°$, $a \approx 6.8$, $c \approx 15.4$

Determine whether each triangle has *no* solution, *one* solution, or *two* solutions. Then solve the triangle. Round side lengths to the nearest tenth and angle measures to the nearest degree if necessary.

14. $A = 29°$, $a = 6$, $b = 13$ **no solution**

15. $A = 70°$, $a = 25$, $b = 20$ **one solution;**
$B \approx 49°$, $C \approx 61°$, $c \approx 23.3$

16. $A = 113°$, $a = 21$, $b = 25$ **no solution**

17. $A = 110°$, $a = 20$, $b = 8$ **one solution;**
$B \approx 22°$, $C \approx 48°$, $c \approx 15.8$

18. $A = 66°$, $a = 12$, $b = 7$ **one solution;**
$B \approx 32°$, $C \approx 82°$, $c \approx 13.0$

19. $A = 54°$, $a = 5$, $b = 8$ **no solution**

20. $A = 45°$, $a = 15$, $b = 18$**two solutions;**
$B \approx 58°$, $C \approx 77°$, $c \approx 20.7$;
$B \approx 122°$, $C \approx 13°$, $c \approx 4.8$

21. $A = 60°$, $a = 4\sqrt{3}$, $b = 8$ **one solution;**
$B \approx 90°$, $C \approx 30°$, $c \approx 4.0$

22. **WILDLIFE** Sarah Phillips, an officer for the Department of Fisheries and Wildlife, checks boaters on a lake to make sure they do not disturb two osprey nesting sites. She leaves a dock and heads due north in her boat to the first nesting site. From here, she turns 5° north of due west and travels an additional 2.14 miles to the second nesting site. She then travels 6.7 miles directly back to the dock. How far from the dock is the first osprey nesting site? Round to the nearest tenth. **6.2 mi**

Page 27 (Word Problem Practice)

13-4 Word Problem Practice

Law of Sines

1. **WALKING** Alliya is taking a walk along a straight road. She decides to leave the road, so she walks on a path that makes an angle of 35° with the road. After walking for 450 meters, she turns 75° and heads back towards the road.

a. How far does Alliya need to walk on her current path to get back to the road? **402 m**

b. When Alliya returns to the road, how far along the road is she from where she started? **676 m**

2. **SAILING** A spinnaker is a large triangular sail that swings out opposite the mainsail, and is used when running with the wind. The *luff* is the leading edge of the sail, the *leach* is the edge away from the wind, and the *foot* is the bottom edge. Find the missing measure for each sail.

Luff (ft)	Leach (ft)	Foot (ft)	Angle between Luff and Leach	Area (ft²)
22	20	14	38°	135.4
28	23.8	18	**40°**	214.1
45	**35**	21	27°	357.5

3. **FISHING** A fishing pole is resting against the railing of a boat making an angle of 22° with the boat's deck. The fishing pole is 5 feet long, and the hook hangs 3 feet from the tip of the pole. The movement of the boat causes the hook to sway back and forth. Determine which angles the fishing line must make with the pole in order for the hook to be level with the boat's deck. **119.4° or 16.6°**

4. **CAMERAS** A security camera is located on top of a building at a certain distance from the sidewalk. The camera revolves counterclockwise at a steady rate of one revolution per minute. At one point in the revolution it directly faces a point on the sidewalk that is 20 meters from the camera. Four seconds later, it directly faces a point 10 meters down the sidewalk.

a. How many degrees does the camera rotate in 4 seconds? **24°**

b. To the nearest tenth of a meter, how far is the security camera from the sidewalk? **19.6 m**

Answers (Lesson 13-4 and Lesson 13-5)

Left Page (28)

NAME _____ DATE _____ PERIOD _____

13-4 Enrichment

Navigation

The bearing of a boat is an angle showing the direction the boat is heading. Often, the angle is measured from north, but it can be measured from any of the four compass directions. At the right, the bearing of the boat is 155°. Or, it can be described as 25° east of south (S25°E).

Example A boat A sights the lighthouse B in the direction N65°E and the spire of a church C in the direction S75°E. According to the map, B is 7 miles from C in the direction N30°W. In order for A to avoid running aground, find the bearing it should keep to pass B at 4 miles distance.

In △ABC, ∠α = 180° − 65° − 75° or 40°
∠C = 180° − 30° − (180° − 75°)
= 45°
a = 7 miles

With the Law of Sines,

$AB = \dfrac{a \sin C}{\sin \alpha} = \dfrac{7(\sin 45°)}{\sin 40°} = 7.7$ mi.

The ray for the correct bearing for A must be tangent at X to circle B with radius BX = 4. Thus △ABX is a right triangle.

Then $\sin \theta = \dfrac{BX}{AB} = \dfrac{4}{7.7} \approx 0.519$. Therefore, ∠θ = 31.3°.

The bearing of A should be 65° − 31.3° or 33.7° east of north.

Exercises

1. Suppose the lighthouse B in the example is sighted at S30°W by a ship P due north of the church C. Find the bearing P should keep to pass B at 4 miles distance. **S64.8°W**

2. In the fog, the lighthouse keeper determines by radar that a boat 18 miles away is heading to the shore. The direction of the lighthouse from the boat is S80°E. What bearing should the lighthouse keeper radio the boat to take to come ashore 4 miles south of the lighthouse? **S68.1°E**

Chapter 13   28   Glencoe Algebra 2

Right Page (29)

NAME _____ DATE _____ PERIOD _____

13-5 Study Guide and Intervention

Law of Cosines

Use Law of Cosines to Solve Triangles

Law of Cosines	Let △ABC be any triangle with a, b, and c representing the measures of the sides, and opposite angles with measures A, B, and C, respectively. Then the following equations are true. $a^2 = b^2 + c^2 - 2bc \cos A$ $b^2 = a^2 + c^2 - 2ac \cos B$ $c^2 = a^2 + b^2 - 2ab \cos C$

You can use the Law of Cosines to solve any triangle if you know the measures of two sides and the included angle (SAS case), or the measures of three sides (SSS case).

Example Solve △ABC.

You are given the measures of two sides and the included angle. Begin by using the Law of Cosines to determine c.

$c^2 = a^2 + b^2 - 2ab \cos C$
$c^2 = 28^2 + 15^2 - 2(28)(15)\cos 82°$
$c^2 \approx 892.09$
$c \approx 29.9$

Next you can use the Law of Sines to find the measure of angle A.

$\dfrac{\sin A}{a} = \dfrac{\sin C}{c}$

$\dfrac{\sin A}{23} \approx \dfrac{\sin 82°}{29.9}$

$\sin A \approx 0.9273$

$A \approx 68°$

The measure of B is about 180° − (82° + 68°) or about 30°.

Exercises

Solve each triangle. Round side lengths to the nearest tenth and angle measures to the nearest degree.

1. a = 14, c = 20, B = 38°
b ≈ 12.4, A ≈ 44°, C ≈ 98°

2. A = 60°, c = 17, b = 12
a ≈ 15.1, B ≈ 43°, C ≈ 77°

3. a = 4, b = 6, c = 3
A ≈ 36°, B ≈ 117°, C ≈ 27°

4. A = 103°, b = 31, c = 52
a ≈ 66, B ≈ 27°, C ≈ 50°

5. a = 15, b = 26, C = 132°
c ≈ 37.7, A ≈ 17°, B ≈ 31°

6. a = 31, b = 52, c = 43
A ≈ 36°, B ≈ 88°, C ≈ 56°

Chapter 13   29   Glencoe Algebra 2

Answers (Lesson 13-5)

Skills Practice page

NAME _____ DATE _____ PERIOD _____

13-5 Skills Practice

Law of Cosines

Solve each triangle. Round side lengths to the nearest tenth and angle measures to the nearest degree.

1.

$B \approx 23°$,
$C \approx 116°$, $a \approx 5.1$

2.

$A \approx 104°$,
$B \approx 47°$, $C \approx 29°$

3.

$A \approx 143°$,
$B \approx 20°$, $C \approx 18°$

4. $C = 71°$, $a = 3$, $b = 4$

$A \approx 44°$,
$B \approx 67°$, $c \approx 4.1$

5. $C = 35°$, $a = 5$, $b = 8$

$A \approx 36°$,
$B \approx 109°$, $c \approx 4.8$

Determine whether each triangle should be solved by beginning with the Law of Sines or the Law of Cosines. Then solve the triangle.

6.

sines; $A \approx 27°$,
$C \approx 119°$, $c \approx 7.8$

7.

cosines; $A \approx 41°$,
$C \approx 55°$, $b \approx 6.1$

8.

sines; $B = 30°$,
$a \approx 2.7$, $c \approx 6.1$

9. $A = 11°$, $C = 27°$, $c = 50$

sines; $B = 142°$,
$a \approx 21.0$, $b \approx 67.8$

10. $B = 47°$, $a = 20$, $c = 24$

cosines; $A \approx 55°$,
$C \approx 79°$, $b \approx 17.9$

11. $A = 71°$, $C = 62°$, $a = 20$

sines; $B = 47°$,
$b \approx 15.5$, $c \approx 18.7$

12. $a = 5$, $b = 12$, $c = 13$

cosines; $A \approx 23°$,
$B \approx 67°$, $C \approx 90°$

13. $A = 51°$, $a = 7$, $c = 10$

cosines; $B \approx 44°$,
$C \approx 85°$, $a \approx 7.8$

14. $a = 13$, $A = 41°$, $B = 75°$

sines; $C = 64°$,
$b \approx 19.1$, $c \approx 17.8$

15. $B = 125°$, $a = 8$, $b = 14$

sines; $A \approx 28°$,
$C \approx 27°$, $c \approx 7.8$

16. $a = 5$, $b = 6$, $c = 7$

cosines; $A \approx 44°$,
$B \approx 57°$, $C \approx 78°$

Study Guide and Intervention page

NAME _____ DATE _____ PERIOD _____

13-5 Study Guide and Intervention (continued)

Law of Cosines

Choose a Method to Solve Triangles

	Given	Begin by Using
Solving an Oblique Triangle	two angles and any side	Law of Sines
	two sides and an angle opposite one of them	Law of Sines
	two sides and their included angle	Law of Cosines
	three sides	Law of Cosines

Example Determine whether △ABC should be solved by beginning with the Law of Sines or Law of Cosines. Then solve the triangle.

You are given the measures of two sides and their included angle, so use the Law of Cosines.

$a^2 = b^2 + c^2 - 2bc \cos A$ Law of Cosines

$a^2 = 20^2 + 8^2 - 2(20)(8) \cos 34°$ $b = 20, c = 8, A = 34°$

$a^2 = 198.71$ Use a calculator to simplify.

$a \approx 14.1$ Use a calculator to simplify.

Use the Law of Sines to find C.

$\dfrac{\sin C}{c} = \dfrac{\sin A}{a}$ Law of Sines

$\sin C = \dfrac{8 \sin 34°}{14.1}$ $c = 8, A = 34° , a = 14.1$

$C \approx 18°$ Use the $\sin^{-1}$ function.

The measure of angle B is approximately $180 - (34° + 18°)$ or about $128°$.

Exercises

Determine whether each triangle should be solved by beginning with the Law of Sines or Law of Cosines. Then solve the triangle.

1.

Law of Sines; $A \approx 108°$,
$B \approx 47°$, $b \approx 13.8$

2.

Law of Cosines; $c \approx$
11.9, $B \approx 15°$, $A \approx 37°$

3.

Law of Cosines; $A \approx$
$74°$, $B \approx 61°$, $C \approx 45°$

4. $A = 58°$, $a = 12$, $b = 8$

Law of Sines; $B \approx 34°$,
$C \approx 88°$, $c \approx 14.1$

5. $a = 28$, $b = 35$, $c = 20$

Law of Cosines; $A \approx$
$53°$, $B \approx 92°$, $C \approx 35°$

6. $A = 82°$, $B = 44°$, $b = 11$

Law of Sines; $a \approx 15.7$,
$c \approx 12.8$, $C \approx 54°$

13-5 Practice

Law of Cosines

Determine whether each triangle should be solved by beginning with the Law of Sines or Law of Cosines. Then solve the triangle.

1. cosines; $c \approx 12.8$, $A \approx 67°$, $B \approx 33°$

2. cosines; $A \approx 36°$, $B \approx 26°$, $C \approx 117°$

3. sines; $B = 60°$, $a \approx 46.0$, $b \approx 40.4$

4. $a = 16$, $b = 20$, $C = 54°$ cosines; $A \approx 51°$, $B \approx 75°$, $c \approx 16.7$

5. $B = 71°$, $c = 6$, $a = 11$ cosines; $A \approx 77°$, $C \approx 32°$, $b \approx 10.7$

6. $A = 37°$, $a = 20$, $b = 18$ sines; $B \approx 33°$, $C \approx 110°$, $c \approx 31.2$

7. $C = 35°$, $a = 18$, $b = 24$ cosines; $A \approx 48°$, $B \approx 97°$, $c \approx 13.9$

8. $a = 8$, $b = 6$, $c = 9$ cosines; $A \approx 61°$, $B \approx 41°$, $C \approx 79°$

9. $A = 23°$, $b = 10$, $c = 12$ cosines; $B \approx 54°$, $C \approx 103°$, $a \approx 4.8$

10. $a = 4$, $b = 5$, $c = 8$ cosines; $A \approx 24°$, $B \approx 31°$, $C \approx 125°$

11. $B = 46.6°$, $C = 112°$, $b = 13$ sines; $A \approx 21.4$, $a \approx 6.5$, $c \approx 16.6$

12. $A = 46.3°$, $a = 35$, $b = 30$ sines; $B \approx 38°$, $C \approx 95°$, $c \approx 48.2$

13. $a = 16.4$, $b = 21.1$, $c = 18.5$ cosines; $A \approx 48°$, $B \approx 74°$, $C \approx 57°$

14. $C = 43.5°$, $b = 8$, $c = 6$ sines; $A \approx 70°$, $B \approx 67°$, $a \approx 8.2$

15. $A = 78.3°$, $b = 7$, $c = 11$ cosines; $B \approx 36°$, $C \approx 66°$, $a \approx 11.8$

16. **SATELLITES** Two radar stations 2.4 miles apart are tracking an airplane. The straight-line distance between Station A and the plane is 7.4 miles. The straight-line distance between Station B and the plane is 6.9 miles. What is the angle of elevation from Station A to the plane? Round to the nearest degree. **69°**

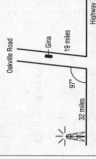

17. **DRAFTING** Marion is using a computer-aided drafting program to produce a drawing for a client. She begins a triangle by drawing a segment 4.2 inches long from point A to point B. From B, she draws a second segment that forms a 42° angle with $\overline{AB}$ and is 6.4 inches long, ending at point C. To the nearest tenth, how long is the segment from C to A? **4.3 in.**

13-5 Word Problem Practice

Law of Cosines

1. **POOLS** The Perth County pool has a lifeguard station in both the deep water and shallow water sections of the pool. The distance between each station and the bottom of the slide is known, but the manager would like to calculate more information about the pool setup.

[Figure: Slide, 38°, 12 yards, 18 yards, Shallow Water Station, Deep Water Station]

a. When the lifeguards switch positions, the lifeguard at the deep water station swims to the shallow water station. How far does the lifeguard swim? **11.3 yards**

b. If the lifeguard at the deepwater station is directly facing the bottom of the slide, what angle does she need to turn in order to face the lifeguard at the shallow water station? **40.9°**

2. **CAMPING** At Shady Pines Campground, Campsites A and B are situated 50 meters apart. The camp office is 55 meters from Campsite A and 15 meters from Campsite B. When the ranger is standing at the office, what is the angle of separation between Campsites A and B? **43.5°**

3. **SKATING** During a figure skating routine, Jackie and Peter skate apart with an angle of 15° between them. Jackie skates for 5 meters and Peter skates for 7 meters. How far apart are the skaters? **2.5 m**

4. **TECHNOLOGY** Gina's handheld PDA can send and receive e-mails if it is within 40 miles of a transmission tower. On a trip, Gina drives past the transmission tower on Highway 7 for 32 miles, and then she turns onto Oakville Road and drives for another 19 miles.

[Figure: Oakville Road, Gina, 19 miles, 97°, 32 miles, Highway 7]

a. Is Gina close enough to the transmission tower to be able to send and receive e-mails? Explain your reasoning. **Yes. She is 39.2 miles from the tower.**

b. If Gina is within range of the tower, how much farther can she drive on Oakville Road before she is out of range? If she is out of range and drives back towards Highway 7, how far will she travel before she is back in range? **She is within range and can drive 1.4 miles farther.**

33   Glencoe Algebra 2

13-5 Enrichment

NAME _____ DATE _____ PERIOD _____

The Law of Cosines and the Pythagorean Theorem

The Law of Cosines bears strong similarities to the Pythagorean Theorem. According to the Law of Cosines, if two sides of a triangle have lengths a and b and if the angle between them has a measure of $x°$, then the length, y, of the third side of the triangle can be found by using the equation

$$y^2 = a^2 + b^2 - 2ab \cos x°.$$

Answer the following questions to clarify the relationship between the Law of Cosines and the Pythagorean Theorem.

1. If the value of $x°$ becomes less and less, what number does $\cos x°$ approach? **1**

2. If the value of $x°$ is very close to zero but then increases, what happens to $\cos x°$ as $x°$ approaches 90°? **decreases, approaches 0**

3. If $x°$ equals 90°, what is the value of $\cos x°$? What does the equation of $y^2 = a^2 + b^2 - 2ab \cos x°$ simplify to if $x°$ equals 90°? **0, $y^2 = a^2 + b^2$**

4. What happens to the value of $\cos x°$ as $x°$ increases beyond 90° and approaches 180°? **decreases to −1**

5. Consider some particular value of a and b, say 7 for a and 19 for b. Use a graphing calculator to graph the equation you get by solving $y^2 = 7^2 + 19^2 - 2(7)(19) \cos x°$ for y. **See students' graphs.**

  a. In view of the geometry of the situation, what range of values should you use for $x°$? **x min = 0°; x max = 180°**

  b. Display the graph and use the TRACE function. What do the maximum and minimum values appear to be for the function? **See students' graphs.**

  c. How do the answers for part b relate to the lengths 7 and 19? Are the maximum and minimum values from part b ever actually attained in the geometric situation? **min = 19 − 7; max = 19 + 7; no**

NAME _____ DATE _____ PERIOD _____

13-6 Study Guide and Intervention

Circular Functions

Circular Functions

Definition of Sine and Cosine	If the terminal side of an angle θ in standard position intersects the unit circle at $P(x, y)$, then $\cos \theta = x$ and $\sin \theta = y$. Therefore, the coordinates of P can be written as $P(\cos \theta, \sin \theta)$.

Example The terminal side of angle θ in standard position intersects the unit circle at $P\left(-\frac{5}{6}, \frac{\sqrt{11}}{6}\right)$. Find $\cos \theta$ and $\sin \theta$.

$P\left(-\frac{5}{6}, \frac{\sqrt{11}}{6}\right) = P(\cos \theta, \sin \theta)$, so $\cos \theta = -\frac{5}{6}$ and $\sin \theta = \frac{\sqrt{11}}{6}$

Exercises

The terminal side of angle θ in standard position intersects the unit circle at each point P. Find $\cos \theta$ and $\sin \theta$.

1. $P\left(-\frac{\sqrt{3}}{2}, \frac{1}{2}\right)$

$\sin \theta = \frac{1}{2}$, $\cos \theta = -\frac{\sqrt{3}}{2}$

2. $P(0, -1)$

$\sin \theta = -1$, $\cos \theta = 0$

3. $P\left(-\frac{2}{3}, \frac{\sqrt{5}}{3}\right)$

$\sin \theta = \frac{\sqrt{5}}{3}$, $\cos \theta = -\frac{2}{3}$

4. $P\left(-\frac{4}{5}, -\frac{3}{5}\right)$

$\cos \theta = -\frac{4}{5}$, $\sin \theta = -\frac{3}{5}$

5. $P\left(\frac{1}{6}, -\frac{\sqrt{35}}{6}\right)$

$\sin \theta = -\frac{\sqrt{35}}{6}$, $\cos \theta = \frac{1}{6}$

6. $P\left(\frac{\sqrt{7}}{4}, \frac{3}{4}\right)$

$\sin \theta = \frac{3}{4}$, $\cos \theta = \frac{\sqrt{7}}{4}$

7. P is on the terminal side of $\theta = 45°$.

$\sin \theta = \frac{\sqrt{2}}{2}$, $\cos \theta = \frac{\sqrt{2}}{2}$

8. P is on the terminal side of $\theta = 120°$.

$\sin \theta = \frac{\sqrt{3}}{2}$, $\cos \theta = -\frac{1}{2}$

9. P is on the terminal side of $\theta = 240°$.

$\sin \theta = -\frac{\sqrt{3}}{2}$, $\cos \theta = -\frac{1}{2}$

10. P is on the terminal side of $\theta = 330°$.

$\sin \theta = -\frac{1}{2}$, $\cos \theta = \frac{\sqrt{3}}{2}$

NAME _____ DATE _____ PERIOD _____

13-6 Skill Practice

Circular Functions

The terminal side of angle θ in standard position intersects the unit circle at each point P. Find $\cos \theta$ and $\sin \theta$.

1. $P\left(\frac{3}{5}, \frac{4}{5}\right)$ $\sin \theta = \frac{4}{5}$

$\cos \theta = \frac{3}{5}$

2. $P\left(\frac{5}{13}, -\frac{12}{13}\right)$ $\sin \theta = -\frac{12}{13}$

$\cos \theta = \frac{5}{13}$

3. $P\left(-\frac{9}{41}, -\frac{40}{41}\right)$ $\sin \theta = -\frac{9}{41}$

$-\frac{40}{41}$, $\cos \theta = -\frac{9}{41}$

4. $P(0, 1)$ $\sin \theta = 1$

$\cos \theta = 0$

5. $P(-1, 0)$ $\sin \theta = 0$,

$\cos \theta = -1$

6. $P\left(\frac{1}{2}, \frac{\sqrt{3}}{2}\right)$ $\sin \theta = \frac{\sqrt{3}}{2}$

$-\frac{\sqrt{3}}{2}$, $\cos \theta = \frac{1}{2}$

Find the exact value of each function.

7. $\cos 45°$ $\frac{\sqrt{2}}{2}$

8. $\sin 210°$ $-\frac{1}{2}$

9. $\sin 330°$ $-\frac{1}{2}$

10. $\cos 330°$ $\frac{\sqrt{3}}{2}$

11. $\cos (-60°)$ $\frac{1}{2}$

12. $\sin (-390°)$ $-\frac{1}{2}$

13. $\sin 5\pi$ 0

14. $\cos 3\pi$ -1

15. $\sin \frac{5\pi}{2}$ 1

16. $\sin \frac{7\pi}{3}$ $\frac{\sqrt{3}}{2}$

17. $\cos \left(-\frac{7\pi}{3}\right)$ $\frac{1}{2}$

18. $\cos \left(-\frac{5\pi}{6}\right)$ $-\frac{\sqrt{3}}{2}$

Determine the period of each function.

19.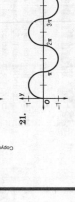

4

20.

2

21.

2π

Chapter 13 37 *Glencoe Algebra 2*

NAME _____ DATE _____ PERIOD _____

13-6 Study Guide and Intervention *(continued)*

Circular Functions

Periodic Functions

A periodic function has y-values that repeat at regular intervals. One complete pattern is called a **cycle**, and the horizontal length of one cycle is called a **period**.

The sine and cosine functions are periodic; each has a period of $360°$ or 2π radians.

Example 1 Determine the period of the function.

The pattern of the function repeats every 10 units, so the period of the function is 10.

Example 2 Find the exact value of each function.

a. $\sin 855°$

$\sin 855° = \sin (135° + 720°)$

$= \sin 135°$ or $\frac{\sqrt{2}}{2}$

b. $\cos \left(\frac{31\pi}{6}\right)$

$\cos \left(\frac{31\pi}{6}\right) = \cos \left(\frac{7\pi}{6} + 4\pi\right)$

$= \cos \frac{7\pi}{6}$ or $-\frac{\sqrt{3}}{2}$

Exercises

Determine the period of each function.

1.

$\frac{5\pi}{2}$

2.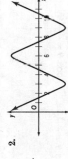

6

Find the exact value of each function.

3. $\sin (-510°)$ $-\frac{1}{2}$

4. $\sin 495°$ $\frac{\sqrt{2}}{2}$

5. $\cos \left(-\frac{5\pi}{2}\right)$ 0

6. $\sin \left(\frac{5\pi}{3}\right)$ $-\frac{\sqrt{3}}{2}$

7. $\cos \left(\frac{11\pi}{4}\right)$ $-\frac{\sqrt{2}}{2}$

8. $\sin \left(-\frac{3\pi}{4}\right)$ $-\frac{\sqrt{2}}{2}$

Chapter 13 36 *Glencoe Algebra 2*

Lesson 13-6

NAME _____ DATE _____ PERIOD _____

13-6 Word Problem Practice

Circular Functions

1. TIRES A point on the edge of a car tire is marked with paint. As the car moves slowly, the marked point on the tire varies in distance from the surface of the road. The height in inches of the point is given by the expression $h = -8\cos t + 8$, where t is the time in seconds.

a. What is the maximum height above ground that the point on the tire reaches? **16 inches**

b. What is the minimum height above ground that the point on the tire reaches? **0 inches**

c. How many rotations does the tire make per second? $\dfrac{1}{2\pi}$

d. How far does the marked point travel in 30 seconds? How far does the marked point travel in one hour? **20 ft; 2400 ft**

2. GEOMETRY The temperature T in degrees Fahrenheit of a city t months into the year is approximated by the formula $T = 42 + 30 \sin\left(\dfrac{\pi}{6}t\right)$.

a. What is the highest monthly temperature for the city? **72°F**

b. In what month does the highest temperature occur? **March**

c. What is the lowest monthly temperature for the city? **12°F**

d. In what month does the lowest temperature occur? **September**

3. THE MOON The Moon's period of revolution is the number of days it takes for the Moon to revolve around Earth. The period can be determined by graphing the percentage of sunlight reflected by the Moon each day, as seen by an observer on Earth. Use the graph to determine the Moon's period of revolution. **approximately 28 days**

Moon's Orbit

(graph: Sunlight Reflected (%) vs Days; x-axis 0, 7, 14, 21, 28, 35)

Chapter 13

39

Glencoe Algebra 2

NAME _____ DATE _____ PERIOD _____

13-6 Practice

Circular Functions

The terminal side of angle θ in standard position intersects the unit circle at each point P. Find $\cos\theta$ and $\sin\theta$.

1. $P\left(-\dfrac{1}{2}, \dfrac{\sqrt{3}}{2}\right)$ $\sin\theta = \dfrac{\sqrt{3}}{2}$, $\cos\theta = -\dfrac{1}{2}$

2. $P\left(\dfrac{20}{29}, -\dfrac{21}{29}\right)$ $\sin\theta = -\dfrac{21}{29}$, $\cos\theta = \dfrac{20}{29}$

3. $P(0.8, 0.6)$ $\sin\theta = 0.6$, $\cos\theta = 0.8$

4. $P(0, -1)$ $\sin\theta = -1$, $\cos\theta = 0$

5. $P\left(-\dfrac{\sqrt{2}}{2}, \dfrac{\sqrt{2}}{2}\right)$ $\sin\theta = \dfrac{\sqrt{2}}{2}$, $\cos\theta = -\dfrac{\sqrt{2}}{2}$

6. $P\left(\dfrac{\sqrt{3}}{2}, \dfrac{1}{2}\right)$ $\sin\theta = \dfrac{1}{2}$, $\cos\theta = \dfrac{\sqrt{3}}{2}$

Determine the period of each function.

7. 4

(graph)

8. 2π

(graph)

Find the exact value of each function.

9. $\cos\dfrac{7\pi}{4}$ $\dfrac{\sqrt{2}}{2}$

10. $\sin(-30°)$ $-\dfrac{1}{2}$

11. $\sin\left(-\dfrac{2\pi}{3}\right)$ $-\dfrac{\sqrt{3}}{2}$

12. $\cos(-330°)$ $\dfrac{\sqrt{3}}{2}$

13. $\cos 600°$ $-\dfrac{1}{2}$

14. $\sin\dfrac{9\pi}{2}$ 1

15. $\cos 7\pi$ -1

16. $\cos\left(-\dfrac{11\pi}{4}\right)$ $-\dfrac{\sqrt{2}}{2}$

17. $\sin(-225°)$ $\dfrac{\sqrt{2}}{2}$

18. $\sin 585°$ $-\dfrac{\sqrt{2}}{2}$

19. $\cos\left(-\dfrac{10\pi}{3}\right)$ $-\dfrac{1}{2}$

20. $\sin 840°$ $\dfrac{\sqrt{3}}{2}$

21. FERRIS WHEELS A Ferris wheel with a diameter of 100 feet completes 2.5 revolutions per minute. What is the period of the function that describes the height of a seat on the outside edge of the Ferris wheel as a function of time? **24 s**

Chapter 13

38

Glencoe Algebra 2

Answers (Lesson 13-6 and Lesson 13-7)

13-7 Study Guide and Intervention

Graphing Trigonometric Functions

Sine, Cosine, and Tangent Functions Trigonometric functions can be graphed on the coordinate plane. Graphs of periodic functions have repeating patterns, or *cycles*; the horizontal length of each cycle is the *period*. The **amplitude** of the graph of a sine or cosine function equals half the difference between the maximum and minimum values of the function. Tangent is a trigonometric function that has asymptotes when graphed.

Parent Function	$y = \sin\theta$	$y = \cos\theta$	$y = \tan\theta$
Sine, Cosine, and Tangent Functions	Domain	(all real numbers)	(all real numbers)	$\{\theta \mid \theta \neq 90 + 180n, n \text{ is an integer}\}$
	Range	$\{y \mid -1 \leq y \leq 1\}$	$\{y \mid -1 \leq y \leq 1\}$	(all real numbers)
	Amplitude	1	1	undefined
	Period	$360°$	$360°$	$180°$

Example Find the amplitude and period of each function. Then graph the function.

a. $y = 4 \cos\frac{\theta}{3}$

First, find the amplitude.

$|a| = |4|$, so the amplitude is 4.

Next find the period.

$\frac{360°}{\left|\frac{1}{3}\right|} = 1080°$

Use the amplitude and period to help graph the function.

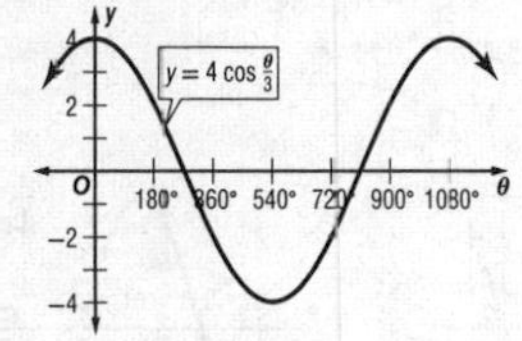

$y = 4 \cos\frac{\theta}{3}$

b. $y = \frac{1}{2} \tan 2\theta$

The amplitude is not defined, and the period is 90°.

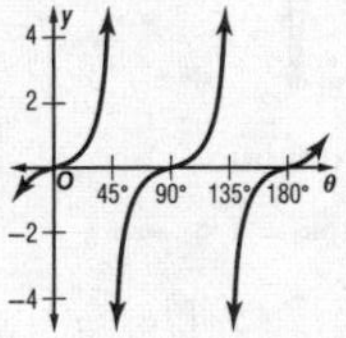

Exercises

Find the amplitude, if it exists, and period of each function. Then graph the function.

1. $y = -4 \sin\theta$ **4; 360°**

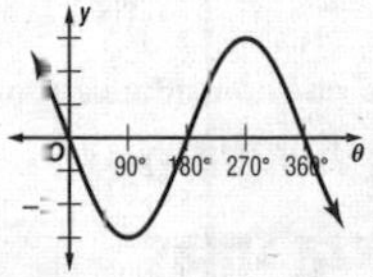

2. $y = 2 \tan\frac{\theta}{2}$ **no amplitude; 360°**

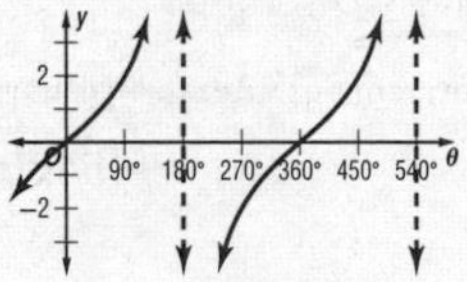

13-6 Enrichment

Polar Coordinates

Consider an angle in standard position with its vertex at a point O called the *pole*. Its initial side is on a coordinated axis called the *polar axis*. A point P on the terminal side of the angle is named by the *polar coordinates* (r, θ) where r is the directed distance of the point from O and θ is the measure of the angle.

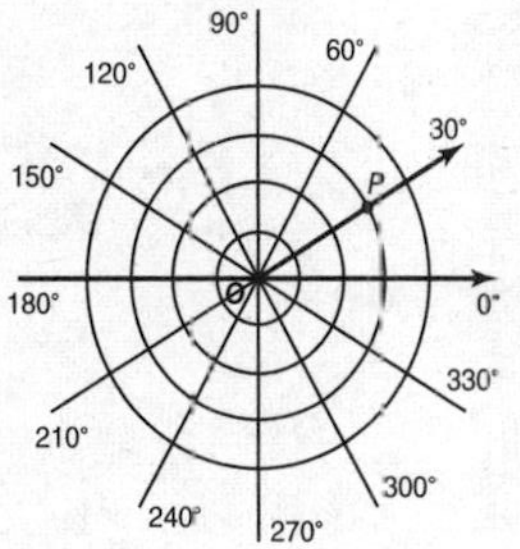

Graphs in this system may be drawn on polar coordinate paper such as the kind shown at the right.

The polar coordinates of a point are not unique. For example, $(3, 30°)$ names point P as well as $(3, 390°)$. Another name for P is $(-3, 210°)$. Can you see why? The coordinates of the pole are $(0, \theta)$ where θ may be any angle.

Example Draw the graph of the function $r = \cos\theta$. Make a table of convenient values for θ and r. Then plot the points.

θ	0°	30°	60°	90°	120°	150°	180°
r	1	$\frac{\sqrt{3}}{2}$	$\frac{1}{2}$	0	$-\frac{1}{2}$	$-\frac{\sqrt{3}}{2}$	-1

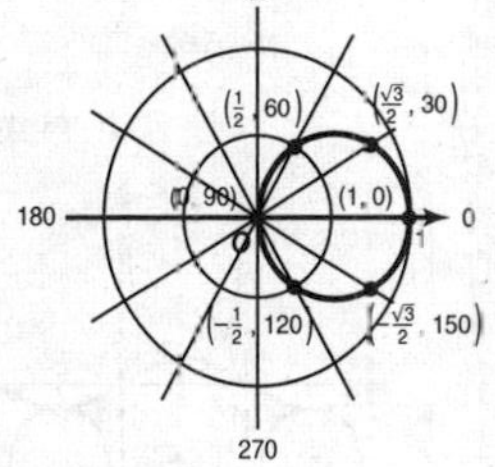

Since the period of the cosine function is 180°, values of r for $\theta > 180°$ are repeated.

Graph each function by making a table of values and plotting the values on polar coordinate paper.

1. $r = 4$

$r = 4$ for all values of θ. Graph should be a circle with radius 4 and center at the pole.

2. $r = 3 \sin\theta$

Graph is circle of radius $\frac{3}{2}$ with center at $\left(\frac{3}{2}, 90°\right)$.

3. $r = 3 \cos 2\theta$

Graph looks like flower with 4 petals, points of petals are at $(3, 0°), (3, 90°), (3, 180°), (3, 270°)$. All petals meet at pole.

4. $r = 2(1 + \cos\theta)$

Graph is heart-shaped curve, symmetric with respect to polar axis.

Lesson 13-7

13-7 Skills Practice

Graphing Trigonometric Functions

Find the amplitude and period of each function. Then graph the function.

1. $y = 2 \cos \theta$

2; 360°

2. $y = 4 \sin \theta$

4; 360°

3. $y = 2 \sec \theta$

no amplitude; 360°

4. $y = \frac{1}{2} \tan \theta$

no amplitude; 180°

5. $y = \sin 3\theta$

1; 120°

6. $y = \csc 3\theta$

no amplitude; 120°

7. $y = \tan 2\theta$

no amplitude; 90°

8. $y = \cos 2\theta$

1; 180°

9. $y = 4 \sin \frac{1}{2}\theta$

4; 720°

13-7 Study Guide and Intervention (continued)

Graphing Trigonometric Functions

Graphs of Other Trigonometric Functions The graphs of the cosecant, secant, and cotangent functions are related to the graphs of the sine, cosine, and tangent functions.

Parent Function	$y = \csc \theta$	$y = \sec \theta$	$y = \cot \theta$
Cosecant, Secant, and Cotangent Functions	Domain	$\{\theta \mid \theta \neq 180n, n$ is an integer$\}$	$\{\theta \mid \theta \neq 90 + 180n, n$ is an integer$\}$	$\{\theta \mid \theta \neq 180n, n$ is an integer$\}$
	Range	$\{y \mid -1 > y$ or $y > 1\}$	$\{y \mid -1 > y$ or $y > 1\}$	{all real numbers}
	Amplitude	undefined	undefined	undefined
	Period	360°	360°	180°

Example Find the period of $y = \frac{1}{2} \csc \theta$. Then graph the function.

Since $\frac{1}{2} \csc \theta$ is a reciprocal of $\frac{1}{2} \sin \theta$, the graphs have the same period, 360°. The vertical asymptotes occur at the points where $\frac{1}{2} \sin \theta = 0$.
So, the asymptotes are at $\theta = 0°$, $\theta = 180°$, and $\theta = 360°$. Sketch $y = \frac{1}{2} \sin \theta$ and use it to graph $y = \frac{1}{2} \csc \theta$.

Exercises

Find the period of each function. Then graph the function.

1. $y = \cot 2\theta$ **90°**

2. $y = \sec 3\theta$ **120°**

NAME _____ DATE _____ PERIOD _____

13-7 Practice

Graphing Trigonometric Functions

Find the amplitude, if it exists, and period of each function. Then graph the function.

1. $y = -4 \sin \theta$
4; 360°

2. $y = \cot \frac{1}{2}\theta$
no amplitude; 360°

3. $y = \cos 5\theta$
1; 72°

4. $y = \csc \frac{3}{4}\theta$
no amplitude; 480°

5. $y = 2 \tan \frac{1}{2}\theta$
no amplitude; 360°

6. $y = \frac{1}{2} \sin \theta$
$\frac{1}{2}$; 360°

7. **FORCE** An anchoring cable exerts a force of 500 Newtons on a pole. The force has the horizontal and vertical components F_x and F_y. (A force of one Newton (N), is the force that gives an acceleration of 1 m/sec² to a mass of 1 kg.)

a. The function $F_x = 500 \cos \theta$ describes the relationship between the angle θ and the horizontal force. What are the amplitude and period of this function? **500; 360°**

b. The function $F_y = 500 \sin \theta$ describes the relationship between the angle θ and the vertical force. What are the amplitude and period of this function? **500; 360°**

8. **WEATHER** The function $y = 60 + 25 \sin \frac{\pi}{6}t$, where t is in months and $t = 0$ corresponds to April 15, models the average high temperature in degrees Fahrenheit in Centerville.

a. Determine the period of this function. What does this period represent?
12; a calendar year

b. What is the maximum high temperature and when does this occur? **85°F; July 15**

NAME _____ DATE _____ PERIOD _____

13-7 Word Problem Practice

Graphing Trigonometric Functions

1. **PHYSICS** The following chart gives functions which model the wave patterns of different colors of light emitted from a particular source, where y is the height of the wave in nanometers and t is the length from the start of the wave in nanometers.

Color	Function
Red	$y = 300 \sin\left(\frac{\pi}{350}t\right)$
Orange	$y = 125 \sin\left(\frac{\pi}{305}t\right)$
Yellow	$y = 460 \sin\left(\frac{\pi}{290}t\right)$
Green	$y = 200 \sin\left(\frac{\pi}{260}t\right)$
Blue	$y = 40 \sin\left(\frac{\pi}{235}t\right)$
Violet	$y = 80 \sin\left(\frac{\pi}{210}t\right)$

a. What are the amplitude and period of the function describing green light waves?
200 nm, 520 nm

b. The intensity of a light wave corresponds directly to its amplitude. Which color emitted from the source is the most intense?
yellow

c. The color of light depends on the period of the wave. Which color has the shortest period? The longest period?
violet, red

2. **SWIMMING** As Charles swims a 25 meter sprint, the position of his right hand relative to the water surface can be modeled by the graph below, where g is the height of the hand in inches from the water level and t is the time in seconds past the start of the sprint. What function describes this graph?

$$y = 8 \sin\left(\frac{4\pi}{5}t\right)$$

3. **ENVIRONMENT** In a certain forest, the leaf density can be modeled by the equation $y = 20 + 15 \sin\left(\frac{\pi}{6}(t-3)\right)$ where y represents the number of leaves per square foot and t represents the month where January = 1.

a. Determine the period of this function. What does this period represent?
The period of the function is 12. This represents one full year.

b. What is the maximum leaf density that occurs in this forest and when does this occur?
35 leaves per square foot, June

Answers (Lesson 13-7 and Lesson 13-8)

13-8 Study Guide and Intervention

Translations of Trigonometric Graphs

Horizontal Translations When a constant is subtracted from the angle measure in a trigonometric function, a **phase shift** of the graph results.

Phase Shift	The phase shift of the graphs of the functions $y = a \sin b(\theta - h)$, $y = a \cos b(\theta - h)$, and $y = a \tan b(\theta - h)$ is h, where $b > 0$. If $h > 0$, the shift is h units to the right. If $h < 0$, the shift is h units to the left.

Example State the amplitude, period, and phase shift for $y = \frac{1}{2} \cos 3\left(\theta - \frac{\pi}{2}\right)$. Then graph the function.

Amplitude: $|a| = \left|\frac{1}{2}\right|$ or $\frac{1}{2}$

Period: $\frac{2\pi}{|b|} = \frac{2\pi}{|3|}$ or $\frac{2\pi}{3}$

Phase Shift: $h = \frac{\pi}{2}$

The phase shift is to the right since $\frac{\pi}{2} > 0$.

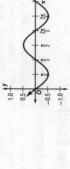

Exercises

State the amplitude, period, and phase shift for each function. Then graph the function.

1. $y = 2 \sin (\theta + 60°)$

2; 360°; 60° to the left

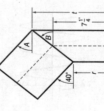

2. $y = \tan \left(\theta - \frac{\pi}{2}\right)$

no amplitude; π; $\frac{\pi}{2}$ to the right

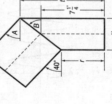

3. $y = 3 \cos (\theta - 45°)$

3; 360°; 45° to the right

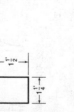

4. $y = \frac{1}{2} \sin 3\left(\theta - \frac{\pi}{3}\right)$

$\frac{1}{2}$; $\frac{2\pi}{3}$; $\frac{\pi}{3}$ to the right

13-7 Enrichment

Blueprints

Interpreting blueprints requires the ability to select and use trigonometric functions and geometric properties. The figure below represents a plan for an improvement to a roof. The metal fitting shown makes a 30° angle with the horizontal. The vertices of the geometric shapes are *not* labeled in these plans. Relevant information must be selected and the appropriate function used to find the unknown measures.

Example Find the unknown measures in the figure at the right.

Roofing Improvement

The measures x and y are the legs of a right triangle.

The measure of the hypotenuse is $\frac{15}{16}$ in. $+ \frac{5}{16}$ in. or $\frac{20}{16}$ in.

$\frac{y}{\frac{20}{16}} = \cos 30°$ $\frac{x}{\frac{20}{16}} = \sin 30°$

$y = 1.08$ in. $x = 0.63$ in.

Find the unknown measures of each of the following. Assume that all angles that appear to be right angles are right angles.

1. Chimney on roof

$y = 3.78'$
$x = 5.72'$
$\angle A = 40°$

2. Air vent

$\angle C = 63.43°$
$\angle D = 26.57°$

3. Elbow joint

$\angle A = 40°$
$\angle B = 50°$
$t = 9.63'$
$r = 4.87'$

NAME _____ DATE _____ PERIOD _____

13-8 Skills Practice

Translations of Trigonometric Graphs

State the amplitude, period, and phase shift for each function. Then graph the function.

1. $y = \sin(\theta + 90°)$

1; 360°; −90°

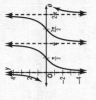

2. $y = \cos(\theta − 45°)$

1; 360°; 45°

3. $y = \tan\left(\theta − \dfrac{\pi}{2}\right)$

no amplitude; π; $\dfrac{\pi}{2}$

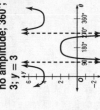

State the amplitude, period, vertical shift, and equation of the midline for each function. Then graph the function.

4. $y = \csc\theta − 2$

no amplitude; 360°; −2; $y = 2$

5. $y = \cos\theta + 1$

1; 360°; 1; $y = 1$

6. $y = \sec\theta + 3$

no amplitude; 360°; 3; $y = 3$

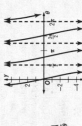

State the amplitude, period, phase shift, and vertical shift of each function. Then graph the function.

7. $y = 2\cos[3(\theta + 45°)] + 2$

2; 120°; −45°; 2

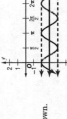

8. $y = 3\sin[2(\theta − 90°)] + 2$

3; 180°; 90°; 2

9. $y = 4\cot\left[\dfrac{4}{3}\left(\theta + \dfrac{\pi}{4}\right)\right] − 2$

no amplitude; $\dfrac{3\pi}{4}$; $−\dfrac{\pi}{4}$; −2

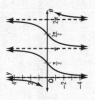

Chapter 13   49   *Glencoe Algebra 2*

NAME _____ DATE _____ PERIOD _____

13-8 Study Guide and Intervention (continued)

Translations of Trigonometric Graphs

Vertical Translations When a constant is added to a trigonometric function, the graph is shifted vertically.

Vertical Shift	The vertical shift of the graphs of the functions $y = a\sin b(\theta − h) + k$, $y = a\cos b(\theta − h) + k$, and $y = a\tan b(\theta − h) + k$ is k. If $k > 0$, the shift is k units up. If $k < 0$, the shift is k units down.

The midline of a vertical shift is $y = k$.

Graphing Trigonometric Functions	**Step 1**	Determine the vertical shift, and graph the midline.
	Step 2	Determine the amplitude, if it exists. Use dashed lines to indicate the maximum and minimum values of the function.
	Step 3	Determine the period of the function and graph the appropriate function.
	Step 4	Determine the phase shift and translate the graph accordingly.

Example State the amplitude, period, vertical shift, and equation of the midline for $y = \cos 2\theta − 3$. Then graph the function.

Amplitude: $|a| = |1|$ or 1

Period: $\dfrac{2\pi}{|b|} = \dfrac{2\pi}{|2|}$ or π

Vertical Shift: $k = −3$, so the vertical shift is 3 units down.

The equation of the midline is $y = −3$.

Since the amplitude of the function is 1, draw dashed lines parallel to the midline that are 1 unit above and below the midline. Then draw the cosine curve, adjusted to have a period of π.

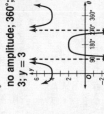

Exercises

State the amplitude, period, vertical shift, and equation of the midline for each function. Then graph the function.

1. $y = \dfrac{1}{2}\cos\theta + 2$

$\dfrac{1}{2}$; 2π; 2 up; $y = 2$

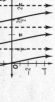

2. $y = 3\sin\theta − 2$

3; 2π; 2 down; $y = −2$

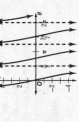

Chapter 13   48   *Glencoe Algebra 2*

Answers (Lesson 13-8)

13-8 Word Problem Practice

Translations of Trigonometric Graphs

1. CLOCKS A town hall has a tower with a clock on its face. The center of the clock is 40 feet above street level. The minute hand of the clock has a length of four feet.

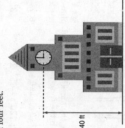

40 ft

a. What is the maximum height of the tip of the minute hand above street level?
44 feet

b. What is the minimum height of the tip of the minute hand above street level?
36 feet

c. Write a sine function that represents the height above street level of the tip of the minute hand for t minutes after midnight.

$$y = 4 \sin\left(\frac{\pi}{30}t + \frac{\pi}{2}\right) + 40$$

d. Graph the function from your answer to part c.

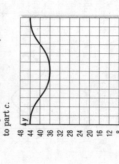

2. ANIMAL POPULATION The population of predators and prey in a closed ecological system tends to vary periodically over time. In a certain system, the population of snakes S can be represented by
$$S = 100 + 20 \sin\left(\frac{\pi}{5}t\right),$$ where t is the number of years since January 1, 2000. In that same system, the population of rats can be represented by
$$R = 200 + 75 \sin\left(\frac{\pi}{5}t + \frac{\pi}{10}\right).$$

a. What is the maximum snake population?
120

b. When is this population first reached?
2.5 yr

c. What is the minimum rat population?
125

d. When is this population first reached?
7 yr

13-8 Practice

Translations of Trigonometric Graphs

State the amplitude, period, phase shift, and vertical shift for each function. Then graph the function.

1. $y = \frac{1}{2}\tan\left(\theta - \frac{\pi}{2}\right)$

no amplitude; π; $\frac{\pi}{2}$; no vertical shift

2. $y = 2\cos(\theta + 30°) + 3$

2; 360°; −30°; 3

3. $y = 3\csc(2\theta + 60°) − 2.5$

no amplitude; 180°; −60°; −2.5

4. $y = -3 + 2\sin 2\left(\theta + \frac{\pi}{4}\right)$

2; π; $-\frac{\pi}{4}$; −3

5. $y = 3\cos 2(\theta + 45°) + 1$

3; 180°; −45°; 1

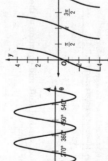

6. $y = -1 + 4\tan(\theta + \pi)$

4; π; $-\pi$; −1

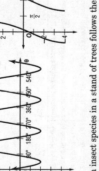

7. ECOLOGY The population of an insect species in a stand of trees follows the growth cycle of a particular tree species. The insect population can be modeled by the function $y = 40 + 30\sin 6t$, where t is the number of years since the stand was first cut in November, 1920.

a. How often does the insect population reach its maximum level?
every 60 yr

b. When did the population last reach its maximum?
1995

c. What condition in the stand do you think corresponds with a minimum insect population?
Sample answer: The species on which the insect feeds has been cut.

Lesson 13-9

13-9 Study Guide and Intervention

NAME _____ DATE _____ PERIOD _____

Inverse Trigonometric Functions

Inverse Trigonometric Functions If you know the value of a trigonometric function for an angle, you can use the *inverse* to find the angle. If you restrict the function's domain, then the inverse is a function. The values in this restricted domain are called **principal values**.

Principal Values of Sine, Cosine, and Tangent	$y = \sin x$ if and only if $y = \sin x$ and $-\frac{\pi}{2} \le x \le \frac{\pi}{2}$.
	$y = \cos x$ if and only if $y = \cos x$ and $0 \le x \le \pi$.
	$y = \tan x$ if and only if $y = \tan x$ and $-\frac{\pi}{2} \le x \le \frac{\pi}{2}$.
Inverse Sine, Cosine, and Tangent	Given $y = \sin x$, the inverse sine function is defined by $y = \sin^{-1} x$ or $y = \arcsin x$.
	Given $y = \cos x$, the inverse cosine function is defined by $y = \cos^{-1} x$ or $y = \arccos x$.
	Given $y = \tan x$, the inverse tangent function is given by $y = \tan^{-1} x$ or $y = \arctan x$.

Example 1   **Find the value of $\sin^{-1}\left(\frac{\sqrt{3}}{2}\right)$. Write angle measures in degrees and radians.**

Find the angle θ for $-\frac{\pi}{2} \le \theta \le \frac{\pi}{2}$ that has a sine value of $\frac{\sqrt{3}}{2}$.

Using a unit circle, the point on the circle that has y-coordinate of $\frac{\sqrt{3}}{2}$ is $\frac{\pi}{3}$ or 60°.

So, $\sin^{-1}\left(\frac{\sqrt{3}}{2}\right) = \frac{\pi}{3}$ or 60°.

Example 2   **Find $\tan\left(\sin^{-1}\frac{1}{2}\right)$. Round to the nearest hundredth.**

Let $\theta = \sin^{-1}\frac{1}{2}$. Then $\sin\theta = \frac{1}{2}$ with $-\frac{\pi}{2} < \theta < \frac{\pi}{2}$. The value $\theta = \frac{\pi}{6}$ satisfies both conditions. $\tan\frac{\pi}{6} = \frac{\sqrt{3}}{3}$ so $\tan\left(\sin^{-1}\frac{1}{2}\right) = \frac{\sqrt{3}}{3}$.

Exercises

Find each value. Write angle measures in degrees and radians.

1. $\cos^{-1}\left(\frac{\sqrt{3}}{2}\right)$ **30°, $\frac{\pi}{6}$**

2. $\sin^{-1}\left(-\frac{\sqrt{3}}{2}\right)$ **−60°, $-\frac{\pi}{3}$**

3. $\arccos\left(-\frac{1}{2}\right)$ **120°, $\frac{2\pi}{3}$**

4. $\arctan\sqrt{3}$ **60°, $\frac{\pi}{3}$**

5. $\arccos\left(-\frac{\sqrt{2}}{2}\right)$ **135°, $\frac{3\pi}{4}$**

6. $\tan^{-1}(-1)$ **−45°, $-\frac{\pi}{4}$**

Find each value. Round to the nearest hundredth if necessary.

7. $\cos\left[\sin^{-1}\left(-\frac{\sqrt{2}}{2}\right)\right]$ **0.71**

8. $\tan\left[\arcsin\left(-\frac{5}{7}\right)\right]$ **−1.02**

9. $\sin\left(\tan^{-1}\frac{5}{12}\right)$ **0.38**

10. $\cos[\arcsin(-0.7)]$ **0.71**

11. $\cos(\arctan 5)$ **0.20**

12. $\sin(\cos^{-1} 0.3)$ **0.95**

Chapter 13   53   *Glencoe Algebra 2*

13-8 Enrichment

NAME _____ DATE _____ PERIOD _____

Simple Harmonic Motion

Suppose a small object is attached to the end of a spring and then released. The object oscillates up and down in a periodic fashion. The motion of the object is known as simple harmonic motion.

The motion of the object is described by the expression $y = A\sin\sqrt{\frac{k}{m}} \, t$, where A is how far down the object is pulled to stretch the spring, k is the spring constant, m is the mass of the object in grams, and t is the time in seconds.

1. A 10-gram object is attached to a spring that has a spring constant of 7, and is released after being pulled down 5 inches. Graph the motion of the spring during the first 10 seconds after the object is dropped.

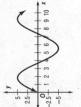

2. How many seconds does it take the object to complete one full oscillation? **about 7.5 seconds**

3. How does the graph in Exercise 1 change as k increases? As k decreases? **As k increases, the period of the graph decreases. As k decreases, the period of the graph increases.**

4. How does the graph in Exercise 1 change as m increases? As m decreases? **As m increases, the period of the graph increases. As m decreases, the period of the graph decreases.**

5. Suppose that while timing the motion of the spring in Exercise 1, the timer was started 1 second early. How would this affect the graph? **Sample Answer: A phase shift of −1 would be introduced.**

Chapter 13   52   *Glencoe Algebra 2*

13-9 Skills Practice

Inverse Trigonometric Functions

Find each value. Write angle measures in degrees and radians.

1. $\sin^{-1}\frac{\sqrt{2}}{2}$ $45°$; $\frac{\pi}{4}$

2. $\cos^{-1}\left(-\frac{\sqrt{3}}{2}\right)$ $150°$; $\frac{5\pi}{6}$

3. $\tan^{-1}\sqrt{3}$ $60°$; $\frac{\pi}{3}$

4. $\arctan\left(-\frac{\sqrt{3}}{3}\right)$ $-30°$; $-\frac{\pi}{6}$

5. $\arccos\left(-\frac{\sqrt{2}}{2}\right)$ $135°$; $\frac{3\pi}{4}$

6. $\arcsin 1$ $90°$; $\frac{\pi}{2}$

Find each value. Round to the nearest hundredth of necessary.

7. $\sin\left(\cos^{-1}1\right)$ 0

8. $\sin\left(\sin^{-1}\frac{1}{2}\right)$ 0.5

9. $\tan\left(\arcsin\frac{\sqrt{3}}{2}\right)$ 1.73

10. $\cos\left(\tan^{-1}3\right)$ 0.32

11. $\sin\left[\arctan(-1)\right]$ -0.71

12. $\sin\left[\arccos\left(-\frac{\sqrt{2}}{2}\right)\right]$ 0.71

Solve each equation. Round to the nearest tenth if necessary.

13. $\cos\theta = 0.25$ $75.5°$

14. $\sin\theta = -0.57$ $-34.8°$

15. $\tan\theta = 5$ $78.7°$

16. $\cos\theta = 0.11$ $83.7°$

17. $\sin\theta = 0.9$ $64.2°$

18. $\tan\theta = -11.35$ $-85.0°$

19. $\sin\theta = 1$ $90°$

20. $\tan\theta = -0.01$ $-0.6°$

21. $\cos\theta = -0.36$ $111.1°$

22. $\tan\theta = -16.6$ $-86.6°$

13-9 Study Guide and Intervention (continued)

Inverse Trigonometric Functions

Solve Equations by Using Inverses You can rewrite trigonometric equations to solve for the measure of an angle.

Example Solve the equation $\sin\theta = -0.25$. Round to the nearest tenth if necessary.

The sine of angle θ is -0.25. This can be written as $\arcsin(-0.25) = \theta$.

Use a calculator to solve.

KEYSTROKES: 2nd [SIN⁻¹] (−) .25 [ENTER] -14.47751219

So, $\theta \approx -14.5°$

Exercises

Solve each equation. Round to the nearest tenth if necessary.

1. $\sin\theta = 0.8$
  $53.1°$

2. $\tan\theta = 4.5$
  $77.5°$

3. $\cos\theta = 0.5$
  $60°$

4. $\cos\theta = -0.95$
  $161.8°$

5. $\sin\theta = -0.1$
  $-5.7°$

6. $\tan\theta = -1$
  $-45°$

7. $\cos\theta = 0.52$
  $58.7°$

8. $\cos\theta = -0.2$
  $101.5°$

9. $\sin\theta = 0.35$
  $20.5°$

10. $\tan\theta = 8$
  $82.9°$

Answers (Lesson 13-9)

NAME _____ DATE _____ PERIOD _____

13-9 Word Problem Practice

Inverse Trigonometric Functions

1. DOORS The exit from a restaurant kitchen has a pair of swinging doors that meet in the middle of the doorway. Each door is three feet wide. A waiter needs to take a cart of plates into the dining area from the kitchen. The cart is two feet wide.

a. What is the minimum angle θ through which the doors must each be opened to prevent the cart from hitting either door? **48.2°**

b. If only one of the two doors could be opened, what is the minimum angle θ through which the door must be opened to prevent the cart from hitting the door? **70.5°**

c. If the pair of swinging doors were replaced by a single door the full width of the opening, what is the minimum angle θ through which the door must be opened to prevent the cart from hitting the door? **48.2°**

2. SURVEYING In ancient times, it was known that a triangle with side lengths of 3, 4, and 5 units was a right triangle. Surveyors used ropes with knots at each unit of length to make sure that an angle was a right angle. Such a rope was placed on the ground so that one leg of the triangle had three knots and the other had four. This guaranteed that the triangle formed was right triangle, meaning that the surveyor had formed a right angle.

To the nearest degree, what are the angle measures in a triangle formed in this way? **37°, 53°, 90°**

3. TRAVEL Beth is riding her bike to her friend Marco's house. She can only ride on the streets, which run north-south or east-west.

a. Beth rides two miles east and four miles south to get to Marco's. If Beth could have traveled directly from her house to Marco's, in what direction would she have traveled? **63.4° south of east**

b. Beth then rides three miles west and one mile north to get to the grocery store. If Beth could have traveled directly from Marco's house to the store, in what direction would she have traveled? **18.4° north of west**

NAME _____ DATE _____ PERIOD _____

13-9 Practice

Inverse Trigonometric Functions

Find each value. Write angle measures in degrees and radians.

1. Arcsin 1   **90°, $\dfrac{\pi}{2}$**

2. $\cos^{-1}\left(-\dfrac{\sqrt{2}}{2}\right)$ **135°, $\dfrac{3\pi}{4}$**

3. $\tan^{-1}\left(-\dfrac{\sqrt{3}}{3}\right)$ **−30°, $-\dfrac{\pi}{6}$**

4. Arccos $\dfrac{\sqrt{2}}{2}$ **45°, $\dfrac{\pi}{4}$**

5. Arctan $(-\sqrt{3})$ **−60°, $-\dfrac{\pi}{3}$**

6. $\sin^{-1}\left(-\dfrac{1}{2}\right)$ **−30°, $-\dfrac{\pi}{6}$**

Find each value. Round to the nearest hundredth if necessary.

7. $\tan\left(\cos^{-1}\dfrac{1}{2}\right)$ **1.73**

8. $\cos\left[\sin^{-1}\left(-\dfrac{3}{5}\right)\right]$ **0.8**

9. $\cos\left[\text{Arctan}\,(-1)\right]$ **0.71**

10. $\tan\left(\sin^{-1}\dfrac{12}{13}\right)$ **2.4**

11. $\sin\left(\text{Arctan}\,\dfrac{\sqrt{3}}{3}\right)$ **0.5**

12. $\cos\left(\text{Arctan}\,\dfrac{3}{4}\right)$ **0.8**

Solve each equation. Round to the nearest tenth if necessary.

13. $\tan\theta = 10$ **84.3°**

14. $\sin\theta = 0.7$ **44.4°**

15. $\sin\theta = -0.5$ **−30.0°**

16. $\cos\theta = 0.05$ **87.1°**

17. $\tan\theta = 0.22$ **12.4°**

18. $\sin\theta = -0.03$ **−1.7°**

19. **PULLEYS** The equation $\cos\theta = 0.95$ describes the angle through which pulley A moves, and $\cos\theta = 0.17$ describes the angle through which pulley B moves. Which pulley moves through a greater angle? **pulley B**

20. **FLYWHEELS** The equation $\tan\theta = 1$ describes the counterclockwise angle through which a flywheel rotates in 1 millisecond. Through how many degrees has the flywheel rotated after 25 milliseconds? **1125°**

NAME _____ DATE _____ PERIOD _____

13-9 Enrichment

Snell's Law

Snell's Law describes what happens to a ray of light that passes from air into water or some other substance. In the figure, the ray starts at the left and makes an angle of incidence θ with the surface.

Part of the ray is reflected, creating an angle of reflection θ. The rest of the ray is bent, or refracted, as it passes through the other medium. This creates angle θ'.

The angle of incidence equals the angle of reflection.

The angles of incidence and refraction are related by Snell's Law:

$$\sin \theta = k \sin \theta'$$

The constant k is called the index of refraction.

k	Substance
1.33	Water
1.36	Ethyl alcohol
1.54	Rock salt and Quartz
1.46–1.96	Glass
2.42	Diamond

Use Snell's Law to solve the following. Round angle measures to the nearest tenth of a degree.

1. If the angle of incidence at which a ray of light strikes the surface of a window is 45° and $k = 1.6$, what is the measure of the angle of refraction? **26.2°**

2. If the angle of incidence of a ray of light that strikes the surface of water is 50°, what is the angle of refraction? **35.2°**

3. If the angle of refraction of a ray of light striking a quartz crystal is 24°, what is the angle of incidence? **38.8°**

4. The angles of incidence and refraction for rays of light were measured five times for a certain substance. The measurements (one of which was in error) are shown in the table. Was the substance glass, quartz, or diamond? **glass**

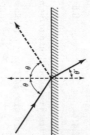

θ	15°	30°	40°	60°	80°
θ'	9.7°	16.1°	21.2°	28.6°	33.2°

5. If the angle of incidence at which a ray of light strikes the surface of ethyl alcohol is 60°, what is the angle of refraction? **39.6°**

Chapter 13 Assessment Answer Key

Quiz 1 (Lessons 13-1 through 13-3)
Page 61

1. $\sin \theta = \frac{8}{17}$; $\cos \theta = \frac{15}{17}$; $\tan \theta = \frac{8}{15}$; $\csc \theta = \frac{17}{8}$; $\sec \theta = \frac{17}{15}$; $\cot \theta = \frac{15}{8}$

2. **B**

3. **Sample answers:** 135°, −585°
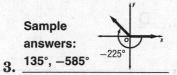

4. **Sample answers:** $\frac{7\pi}{3}, -\frac{5\pi}{3}$

5. $\sin \theta - \frac{\sqrt{10}}{10}$; $\cos \theta = -\frac{3\sqrt{10}}{10}$; $\tan \theta = -\frac{1}{3}$; $\csc \theta = \sqrt{10}$; $\sec \theta = \frac{\sqrt{10}}{3}$; $\cot \theta = -3$

Quiz 2 (Lessons 13-4 and 13-5)
Page 61

1. **D**

2. Law of Sines; $B \approx 99.3°$, $C \approx 30.7°$, $b \approx 11.6$

3. Law of Cosines; $A \approx 46.6°$, $B \approx 104.5°$, $C \approx 28.9°$

4. Law of Cosines; $B \approx 26.3°$, $C \approx 117.7°$, $a \approx 8.0°$

5. Law of Cosines; no solution

Quiz 3 (Lessons 13-6 and 13-7)
Page 62

1. **B**

2. **5**

3. **π**

4. $\frac{3}{4}$; 720° or 4π

5. no amplitude; 180° or π

Quiz 4 (Lessons 13-8 and 13-9)
Page 62

1. amplitude: 2. period: 270° or $\frac{3\pi}{2}$, vertical shift: −1, phase shift: $-\frac{3\pi}{2}$

2. no amplitude; period: 216° or $\frac{6\pi}{5}$, vertical shift: 2, phase shift: 45°

3. **0°**

4. **0.8**

5. **C**

Mid-Chapter Test
Page 63

1. **B**

2. **G**

3. **A**

4. **H**

5. **B**

6. **G**

7. $\sin \theta = \frac{\sqrt{55}}{8}$; $\cos \theta = \frac{3}{8}$; $\tan \theta = \frac{\sqrt{55}}{3}$; $\csc \theta = \frac{8\sqrt{55}}{55}$; $\sec \theta = \frac{8}{3}$; $\cot \theta = \frac{3\sqrt{55}}{55}$

8. $B = 50°$, $a \approx 8.4$, $c \approx 13.1$

9. $\sin \theta = \frac{2\sqrt{5}}{5}$; $\cos \theta = -\frac{\sqrt{5}}{5}$; $\tan \theta = -2$; $\csc \theta = \frac{\sqrt{5}}{2}$; $\sec \theta = \sqrt{5}$; $\cot \theta = -\frac{1}{2}$

10. **1359.1 ft²**

11. one; $B \approx 19.7°$, $C \approx 108.3°$, $c \approx 8.4$

12. **no solution**

Answers

Chapter 13 Assessment Answer Key

Vocabulary Test
Page 64

1. ___e___

2. ___h___

3. ___g___

4. ___c___

5. ___j___

6. ___i___

7. ___a___

8. ___b___

9. ___d___

10. ___f___

11. **Sample answer:**
The position of an
angle if its vertex is
at the origin and its
initial side is on the
positive *x*-axis is its
standard position.

12. **Sample answer:**
A unit circle is a
circle with center at
the origin and
radius 1.

Form 1
Page 65

1. ___A___

2. ___G___

3. ___B___

4. ___F___

5. ___B___

6. ___G___

7. ___B___

8. ___J___

9. ___C___

10. ___G___

Page 66

11. ___D___

12. ___F___

13. ___D___

14. ___H___

15. ___B___

16. ___J___

17. ___B___

18. ___J___

19. ___B___

20. ___J___

B: ___23.3 m___

Chapter 13 Assessment Answer Key

Form 2A
Page 67

Page 68

Form 2B
Page 69

Page 70

1. C

2. G

3. B

4. H

5. A

6. G

7. A

8. F

9. C

10. G

11. B

12. G

13. D

14. F

15. C

16. H

17. C

18. F

19. D

20. H

B: **234 ft**

1. A

2. J

3. B

4. G

5. C

6. G

7. A

8. F

9. A

10. H

11. B

12. J

13. A

14. G

15. D

16. F

17. A

18. H

19. C

20. H

B: **172 ft**

Answers

Chapter 13 Assessment Answer Key

Form 2C
Page 71

$\sin \theta = \frac{5}{13}$; $\cos \theta = \frac{12}{13}$;

$\tan \theta = \frac{5}{12}$; $\csc \theta = \frac{13}{5}$;

$\sec \theta = \frac{13}{12}$; $\cot \theta = \frac{12}{5}$

1. _____

2. $A \approx 25°$; $B \approx 65°$, $b \approx 6.3$

3. $\sin x° = \frac{7}{12}$; $x \approx 36$

4. $-\frac{5\pi}{12}$

5. $300°$

Sample answers:

6. $\frac{13\pi}{4}$, $-\frac{3\pi}{4}$

7. $\sin \theta = -\frac{3\sqrt{13}}{13}$;

$\cos \theta = -\frac{2\sqrt{13}}{13}$;

$\tan \theta = \frac{3}{2}$; $\csc \theta = -\frac{\sqrt{13}}{3}$;

$\sec \theta = -\frac{\sqrt{13}}{2}$; $\cot \theta = \frac{2}{3}$

8.

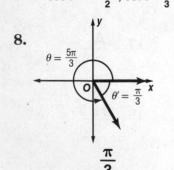

$\frac{\pi}{3}$

9. $-\frac{\sqrt{3}}{2}$

10. 0

11. 635.9 mi^2

Page 72

12. one; $B \approx 36.8°$, $C \approx 85.2°$, $c \approx 20.0$

13. no solution

14. Law of Sines; $C \approx 30°$, $b \approx 9.4$, $c \approx 4.8$

15. Law of Cosines; $A \approx 26.6°$, $B \approx 38.8°$, $c \approx 10.2$

16. $\sin \theta = -\frac{\sqrt{3}}{2}$; $\cos \theta = -\frac{1}{2}$

17. no amplitude, $480°$, $\frac{\pi}{4}$, -1

18. 8π

19. $-45°$ or $-\frac{\pi}{4}$

20. 0.50

B: 56 ft

Chapter 13 Assessment Answer Key

Form 2D
Page 73

1. $\sin\theta = \dfrac{40}{41}$; $\cos\theta = \dfrac{9}{41}$;
$\tan\theta = \dfrac{40}{9}$; $\csc\theta = \dfrac{41}{40}$;
$\sec\theta = \dfrac{41}{9}$; $\cot\theta = \dfrac{9}{40}$

2. $A = 39°$; $B \approx 51$, $b \approx 6.2$

3. $\tan x° = \dfrac{9}{5}$; $x \approx 61$

4. $\dfrac{11\pi}{6}$

5. $-315°$

6. **Sample answers:** $240°$, $-480°$

7. $\sin\theta = -\dfrac{2\sqrt{13}}{13}$; $\cos\theta = \dfrac{3\sqrt{13}}{13}$;
$\tan\theta = -\dfrac{2}{3}$; $\csc\theta = -\dfrac{\sqrt{13}}{2}$;
$\sec\theta = \dfrac{\sqrt{13}}{3}$; $\cot\theta = -\dfrac{3}{2}$

8.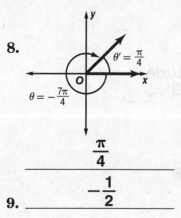
$\theta' = \dfrac{\pi}{4}$
$\theta = -\dfrac{7\pi}{4}$
$\dfrac{\pi}{4}$

9. $-\dfrac{1}{2}$

10. 1

11. 47.7 yd^2

Page 74

12. no solution

13. one; $B \approx 35.3°$, $C \approx 84.7°$, $c \approx 10.3$

14. Law of Sines; $B \approx 15.1°$, $C \approx 145.9°$, $c \approx 17.2$

15. Law of Cosines; $A \approx 24.6°$, $B \approx 110.4°$, $c \approx 6.8$

16. $\sin\theta = -\dfrac{1}{2}$; $\cos\theta = \dfrac{\sqrt{3}}{2}$

17. 2, $270°$, $-90°$, -2

18. 6π

19. $30°$ or $\dfrac{\pi}{6}$

20. 0.38

B: 60 ft

Answers

Chapter 13 Assessment Answer Key

1. $\sin \theta = \frac{2\sqrt{3}}{13}$; $\cos \theta = \frac{3\sqrt{3}}{13}$; $\tan \theta = \frac{2}{3}$; $\csc \theta = \frac{\sqrt{13}}{2}$; $\sec \theta = \frac{\sqrt{13}}{3}$; $\cot \theta = \frac{3}{2}$

2. $A = 65°$; $b \approx 1.2$, $c \approx 2.9$

3. $A \approx 53°$; $B \approx 37°$, $a = 8.0$, $c = 10.0$

4. $-\dfrac{7\pi}{4}$

5. $\left(\dfrac{-900}{\pi}\right)° \approx -286.5°$

6. **Sample answers:** $3°$, $-357°$

7. $\sin \theta = \frac{1}{2}$; $\cos \theta = -\frac{\sqrt{3}}{2}$; $\tan \theta = -\frac{\sqrt{3}}{3}$; $\csc \theta = 2$; $\sec \theta = -\frac{2\sqrt{3}}{3}$; $\cot \theta = -\sqrt{3}$

8. $\dfrac{1}{2}$

9. 1

10. 26.1 m^2

11. two; $B \approx 63.1°$, $C \approx 74.9°$, $c \approx 13.0$; $B \approx 116.9°$, $C \approx 21.1°$, $c \approx 4.8$

12. one; $B \approx 36.9°$, $C \approx 84.1°$, $c \approx 11.6$

13. Law of Cosines; $A \approx 18.2°$, $B \approx 121.7°$, $c \approx 6.2$

14. Law of Sines; $A \approx 25.4°$, $B \approx 22.6°$, $b \approx 13.4$

15. $\sin \theta = \frac{\sqrt{21}}{7}$, $\cos \theta = -\frac{2\sqrt{7}}{7}$

16. $-\dfrac{1}{2}$

17. $-\dfrac{3\sqrt{3}}{4}$

18. 5π

19. no amplitude, $105°$, $-45°$, 5

20. -0.28

B: 51.8 m

Chapter 13 Assessment Answer Key

Page 77, Extended-Response Test
Scoring Rubric

Score	General Description	Specific Criteria
4	**Superior** A correct solution that is supported by well-developed, accurate explanations	• Shows thorough understanding of the concepts of *solving problems involving right triangles, finding values of trigonometric functions for general angles, using reference angles, applying the Laws of Sines and Cosines,* and *solving equations using inverse trigonometric functions.* • Uses appropriate strategies to solve problems. • Computations are correct. • Written explanations are exemplary. • Goes beyond requirements of some of or all problems.
3	**Satisfactory** A generally correct solution, but may contain minor flaws in reasoning or computation	• Shows an understanding of the concepts of *solving problems involving right triangles, finding values of trigonometric functions for general angles, using reference angles, applying the Laws of Sines and Cosines,* and *solving equations using inverse trigonometric functions.* • Uses appropriate strategies to solve problems. • Computations are mostly correct. • Written explanations are effective. • Satisfies all requirements of problems.
2	**Nearly Satisfactory** A partially correct interpretation and/or solution to the problem	• *Shows an understanding of most of the concepts of solving problems involving right triangles, finding values of trigonometric functions for general angles, using reference angles, applying the Laws of Sines and Cosines,* and *solving equations using inverse trigonometric functions.* • May not use appropriate strategies to solve problems. • Computations are mostly correct. • Written explanations are satisfactory. • Satisfies the requirements of most of the problems.
1	**Nearly Unsatisfactory** A correct solution with no supporting evidence or explanation	• Final computation is correct. • No written explanations or work is shown to substantiate the final computation. • Satisfies minimal requirements of some of the problems.
0	**Unsatisfactory** An incorrect solution indicating no mathematical understanding of the concept or task, or no solution is given	• Shows little or no understanding of most of the concepts of *solving problems involving right triangles, finding values of trigonometric functions for general angles, using reference angles, applying the Laws of Sines and Cosines,* and *solving equations using inverse trigonometric functions.* • Does not use appropriate strategies to solve problems. • Computations are incorrect. • Written explanations are unsatisfactory. • Does not satisfy requirements of problems. • No answer may be given.

Answers

Chapter 13 Assessment Answer Key

Page 77, Extended-Response Test
Sample Answers

In addition to the scoring rubric found on page A32, the following sample answers may be used as guidance in evaluating open-ended assessment items.

1a. Students should indicate that knowing the measures of the angles of a triangle gives no information about the lengths of its sides.

1b. Students should explain that Monica can determine the length b since it does not involve measuring across the body of water.

1c. Sample answer: For $A = 115°$, $B = 25°$, $C = 40°$, and $b = 1000$ yd, the Law of Sines gives $\frac{\sin 25°}{1000} = \frac{\sin 40°}{c}$, so $c \approx 1521$ yd.

2. Ideally, students should apply three of the following methods: the Pythagorean Theorem, the Law of Sines, the Law of Cosines, a right triangle trigonometry formula/definition, to find $x \approx 6.1$. (Students may, however, apply two different right triangle formulas and the Pythagorean Theorem as their three methods, for example.)
Sample answers:
By the Pythagorean Theorem, $x^2 + 13.7^2 = 15^2$.
By the Law of Sines, $\frac{\sin 24°}{x} = \frac{\sin 90°}{15}$
By the Law of Cosines, $x^2 = 15^2 + 13.7^2 - 2(15)(13.7)\cos 24°$.
By right triangle trigonometry, $\sin 24° = \frac{x}{15}$.

3. Sample answer: For $P(-3, -4)$, $x = -3$ and $y = -4$, so $\tan \theta = \frac{4}{3}$. This means that $\theta' = \tan^{-1}\left(\frac{4}{3}\right) \approx 53°$ is the reference angle for the angle θ in Quadrant III. Thus, $\theta \approx 180° + 53° = 233°$.

4. For any point $Q(x, y)$ chosen, students should use the relationship $r = \sqrt{x^2 + y^2}$, or the distance formula, to find the radius of the sector r. Then, students should use an inverse trigonometric function to find θ in radians. Finally, students should substitute these values for r and θ into the given formula.
Sample answer: For $Q(3, 4)$,
$r = \sqrt{3^2 + 4^2} = 5$,
$\theta = \tan^{-1}\left(\frac{4}{3}\right) \approx 0.9273$, so
$A \approx \frac{1}{2}(5^2)(0.9273) \approx 11.6$ square units.

5a. Students should explain that they must find the length of another side of the triangle to be able to apply the given formula. They must apply the Law of Sines to determine that $B = 90°$. This gives $A = 45°$ and $a = 9\sqrt{2}$ in. Applying the given formula,
area $= \frac{1}{2}(9\sqrt{2})(9\sqrt{2})\sin 90°$ or
area $= \frac{1}{2}(9\sqrt{2})(18)\sin 45°$, so
area $= 81$ in^2.

5b. Since $\triangle ABC$ is a right triangle, it is possible to apply the formula, so
area $= \frac{1}{2}$(base)(height)
$= \frac{1}{2}(9\sqrt{2})(9\sqrt{2}) = 81$ in^2.

5c. The formula area $= \frac{1}{2}$(base)(height) is a special case of the formula area $= \frac{1}{2}ab \sin C$, where C is a right angle, so $\sin C = 1$.

Chapter 13 Assessment Answer Key

Standardized Test Practice

Page 78

1. Ⓐ Ⓑ Ⓒ ●

2. ● Ⓖ Ⓗ Ⓙ

3. Ⓐ ● Ⓒ Ⓓ

4. Ⓕ ● Ⓗ Ⓙ

5. ● Ⓑ Ⓒ Ⓓ

6. Ⓕ Ⓖ ● Ⓙ

7. Ⓐ Ⓑ Ⓒ ●

8. Ⓕ ● Ⓗ Ⓙ

9. ● Ⓑ Ⓒ Ⓓ

10. Ⓕ Ⓖ Ⓗ ●

Page 79

11. Ⓐ ● Ⓒ Ⓓ

12. ● Ⓖ Ⓗ Ⓙ

13. Ⓐ Ⓑ ● Ⓓ

14. Ⓕ Ⓖ ● Ⓙ

15. 16. 17. 18.

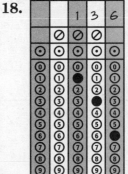

Answers

Chapter 13 Assessment Answer Key

19. $\left\{a \mid -\dfrac{7}{2} \le a \le -\dfrac{3}{2}\right\}$,

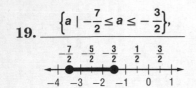

20.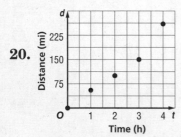

21. **Sample answer: using (2, 100) and (3, 150); $y = 50x$; 300 mi**

22. **consistent and independent**

23. $t \ge 0;\ b \ge 100;\ b + t \le 600$

24. **500**

25. **(−1, 2, −3)**

26. $\begin{bmatrix} -3 & 6 \\ 0 & 6 \end{bmatrix}$

27. **−40**